DRAGON DOCTOR

Further adventures of a zoovet

Also by David Taylor:

Zoovet
Doctor in the Zoo
Going Wild
Next Panda, Please
The Wandering Whale

Dragon Doctor

Further adventures of a zoovet

DAVID TAYLOR

London
GEORGE ALLEN & UNWIN
Boston Sydney

**George Allen & Unwin (Publishers) Ltd,
40 Museum Street, London WC1A 1LU, UK**

George Allen & Unwin (Publishers) Ltd,
Park Lane, Hemel Hempstead, Herts HP2 4TE, UK

George Allen & Unwin Australia Pty Ltd,
8 Napier Street, North Sydney, NSW 2060, Australia

First published in 1985

ISBN 0 04 925032 9

Typeset in 11 on 13 point Baskerville by
Nene Phototypesetters Ltd, Northampton
Printed and bound in Great Britain by
Anchor Brendon Ltd, Tiptree, Essex

To Hannelore,

who puts up with serpents in
the kitchen and sea-lions being
given enemas in the back garden.

Contents

Go, from the creatures thy instructions take:
Learn from the birds what foods the thickets yield;
Learn from the beasts the physic of the field;
Thy arts of building from the bee receive;
Learn of the mole to plough, the worm to weave;
Learn of the little nautilus to sail,
Spread the thin oar, and catch the driving gale.

Pope, *Essay on Man*

1 The Skin of Her Teeth

Like prawns leaving their rocky hidey-holes as the last wisps of daylight dissolve in the darkened sea, the tourists around the Plaza Gomila were emerging. Primed with fizzy sweet wine and rum and coke and fuelled with food that was either fake Spanish or imitation English or an impossibly over-oiled, under-garlicked compromise between the two, they were off, lobster-pink, showered and heavy with Blue Stratos or Avon, to make merry in the pubs that tried to make them feel they had never left home and the discotheques that looked, sounded and smelled just like their counterparts in Birmingham, Düsseldorf or Copenhagen. They were ready for the adventures of the night – the ephemeral romances with the golden Scandinavian girls and the dark young men, seasonal satyrs in waiters' uniforms, the hip gear of disc jockeys and the blazers of tour guides. They were ready for the cloying cocktails no landlord in Barnsley or Bielefeld would be seen dead with. They were ready for the hawkers of golden jewellery, lottery tickets, flowers and photographs with a mournful-looking monkey, for the singsong (our mob and 'Vive España' drowning the German blokes at the other table with 'Ninety-nine Red Balloons') and the wine that the waiter would try in vain to teach them to drink from a *porron* and the consequent hangover that would be slept off on the beach tomorrow. What they were *not* ready for was the great beast that, high as a kite on valium, lurched along the pavement, its sleek fur glowing purple and yellow in the neon glare from Paco's 'El Topless' bar. A 300-pound adult female Patagonian sea-lion was definitely something worth writing home about.

Nina the sea-lion kept moving – we, a handful of my friends from the Marineland at Palma Nova and myself, shooed her along from behind.

'Well! Look at that, that – what is it, Eric? Quick ger a picture – ay, int it bonny! Has it been washed up d'ya think?'

The tourists made way for Nina's lumbering caterpillar-like progress. She ignored them as she passed.

'Can I stroke her?' called a girl in a white mini-skirt and matching first-degree solar burns plastered with Nivea.

'Best not,' I cautioned.

'Oh whar a shame – she's lovely!'

What the holidaymakers didn't know – indeed there was little abnormal to see in the flickering gloom – was that Nina had been punched hard on her jaw, but if she'd lingered for a moment in the lighted doorway of the 'Besame' discotheque they might have noticed the rather cute pout of her lower lip – the only external sign that her jawbone had been shattered in a lovers' tiff. Billy, the massive Patagonian male in the sea-lion breeding pool at Marineland, was like most of his kind, a macho rather overbearing character proud of his fine head and bull-like neck with its handsome ruff of fur. Where Californian sea-lions have pointed, aristocratic faces, their South American cousins possess broader more bucolic features. Billy looks a jolly fellow with his snub-nose, large, rolling intelligent eyes and repertoire of snuffles, snorts and throaty guffaws that wouldn't seem out of place in a clubman's smoking room. But mature sea-lion bulls of all species are martinets who laud it over their harems of females in the epitome of chauvinism. It's very much 'don't speak until you're spoken to, know your place, wait till your elders and betters have finished, and never never answer back' in the Victorian world of Billy and his ilk. Trouble was, Nina must have said or done something – answered back? –

that caused the old man to see red that afternoon. Never one to beat about the bush, Billy had lunged at Nina with his massive lumpy head in the sort of butting movement known to football hooligans and others in Liverpool as the 'Kirby Kiss'. The one butt hadn't been followed up with crushing bites from his powerful jaws – it wasn't a serious fight – but the blow had been strong enough and delivered to the side of Nina's face. Without a murmur – I've never known a sea-lion cry, moan or scream with pain – Nina retreated and when Marcus the sea-lion trainer walked by a few moments later he saw immediately that something was badly wrong. Nina couldn't open or shut her mouth properly and there was a tiny trickle of blood from her lips. Marcus offered her a herring and then a mackerel. He tried a fresh cuttlefish. Nina, normally more gourmand than gourmet, turned her head away and went to lie down in the shade.

Half an hour later I was on my way to London Airport to catch the last flight to Palma. Nina the sea-lion was a recent gift from the great Sea World of San Diego, USA, and one of Marineland's gentlest creatures. Robert Bennett, the Director, wanted me out at once. Nothing could be allowed to happen to Nina – but it looked very much as if it had. And Robert suspected the worst – rightly as it was to turn out.

As usual, after receiving the 'phone call from Marineland and getting the guts of the history of the case, I took time on the two-hour flight to Majorca to consider the possibilities. My journeys generally give breathing space for such armchair theorising; it depends a lot on having received a meaningful and accurate report, but generally I am dealing with professionals used to observing animals objectively and there is rarely any hysteria, raging or weeping on the other end of the telephone and I get enough information to chew on before I arrive. I can review the alternative anaesthetic and drug choices, their dosages, side-effects and contra-indications for the species involved, consider – if I know the place – where and how the patient might be examined, operated upon, hospitalised and so forth. And I can mentally lay out the various diagnostic possibilities and their treatment. It's rather like spreading a set of playing cards and arraying them in suits and numerical order – in the mind.

It was 1983 and I was still the veterinary fireman of the international zoo world. Have dart gun, will travel. Andrew had now been my partner for ten years and the practice continued to grow, encompassing the richest variety of rare and high-value animals from Greenland to Africa, from Arabia to the Far East. In Europe, we were always on the move on a line running down from the Baltic south through Germany and splitting in Switzerland into two paths – one south-west across France and Spain and the other south-east to the heel of Italy. On the map it would have made sense to base ourselves in Zurich – the geographical hub of our practice. But Andrew remained attached to Yorkshire and his house near Keighley, able to fly out of Manchester or Leeds, and I was happily ensconced in Lightwater, a twenty-minute drive from London's Heathrow Airport. Our assistant, Chris Furley, was completing his fourth year at the Al Ain Oasis Zoo on the Abu Dhabi–Oman border and was rapidly developing into an authority on the problems of the diminutive and delightful Arabian gazelle. No, I couldn't imagine us ever emigrating to Switzerland. So, as the Iberia flight passed over the English coast, I closed my eyes and looked back across the years to the beginning of it all at the once bustling Manchester Zoo, Belle Vue – now a wasteland of dreary housing estates, with banal street names like 'Ellen Wilkinson Crescent' rather than 'Wallaby Walk'. Ah, the tigers and elephants and bisons that still roamed there for me and some of whose bones must doubtless have been exhumed by the importunate bulldozers. One of the last buildings to be demolished in the Zoo had been the old Victorian sea-lion house – the stronghold, when I had started zoo medicine in the mid-fifties, of the formidable Mrs

Schmidt and her 'boys', a bunch of Californian sea-lions that she once poisoned accidentally with archaic worming medicine. Throughout the intervening years I'd examined sick and injured sea-lions all over the world and I searched my memory for the cases of head and particularly mouth injury.

The teeth of a sea-lion are sharp and strong and their jaw muscles are more powerful than any bulldog's. I'd seen innumerable bite wounds as a result of mouth to mouth combat between quarrelling or merely tetchy animals. Some of the torn lips, broken teeth and gouged cheeks had required careful antibiotic treatment to combat infection that developed later. Sea-lion mouths teem with germs of one sort or another. Indeed they have a bite which I consider 'dirtier' than even that of humans, crocodiles or chimpanzees – species that carry in the normal 'healthy' mouth a frightening selection of bacteria and other organisms which mean hospital treatment for even the smallest wound. They are more likely to become septic than monkey bites, even though healthy monkeys often carry the bugs responsible for scarlet fever, diphtheria and rheumatic fever in their mouths. Sea-lion bites on humans I always treat with great respect – unlike most hospital casualty departments who generally class sea-lions along with dogs and give nothing more than penicillin and an anti-tetanus shot. The germs of the sea-lion mouth, however, are potentially far more dangerous than those you might come across in Towser's dentures, including one that is the cause of the notorious 'blubber finger' or 'seal hand' so dreaded by the old time whalers and seal skinners. This bacterium (or bacteria – there may be two – one of which is as yet unidentified) produces such a painful inflamation of the bitten area that men have been known to chop off their fingers or hands in order to be rid of the raging agony. Nowadays we tackle such infection successfully with tetracyclines. I could remember a handful of cases where squabbling had resulted in a sea-lion dislocating his jaw – remedied, as in humans, by giving a deep sedative and then levering the errant mandible back into place often with the help of a sharp blow to the chin. In the early days anaesthesia of pinnipeds, the seal, sea-lion and walrus family, had been a terrible worry. Getting a mask on to a powerful animal that could hold its breath for many minutes at a time was even more of a problem where facial injury had occurred. And barbiturate injections had proved very risky. For my first cases of 'mugged' sea-lions I'd used the curare-like drugs, which act in the same way as South American Indian arrow poisons, paralysing the muscles but not obliterating pain. Imperfect though this method had been, it had allowed me to complete the quick manoeuvre of clicking the jaw back into place on a number of occasions. Broken jaws were another matter. In twenty years I had only seen two sea-lions with such an injury. One, a stranded youngster found on a Mexican beach with a neat fracture exactly at the place where the two arms of the lower jaw meet at the point of the chin, had done well after we had bound the left and right fang teeth together with stainless steel wire, first filing a shallow groove in the outer surface of each tooth in order to seat the wire securely. The little animal looked just like any American school kid with braces on his teeth when he swallowed fish during the five weeks that the mouth took to heal.

The other case had been very much a different kettle of fish. A psychopath armed with a .22 rifle had got into the small seaside zoo at Cleethorpes in Lincolnshire and taken pot shots at half a dozen animals before the alarm had been raised and he'd got away leaving behind several dead swans, a mortally wounded monkey and a bull sea-lion with a bleeding hole in the side of his face and a lower jaw that was plainly askew. When I arrived to examine him I'd had the sea-lion trapped in a corner of his indoor quarters behind two stout wooden boards where he hadn't put up much of a struggle. His face was already severely swollen and he hadn't eaten or drunk anything for almost twenty-four hours. I was able to slip a shot of phencyclidine into him through a gap between the boards. The drug certainly knocked the big animal out but was by no means an ideal anaesthetic for sea-lions. His body quivered constantly and the flesh was tense and resistant. But at the time we'd nothing better for these difficult patients. To relax him more I gave him atropine and some intravenous pentothal but although unconscious he had continued trembling. The sea-lion's jaw was broken jaggedly at the point where the bullet had entered. No place for a plaster cast or a splint – I had to operate. It wasn't easy wielding scalpel and forceps on a patient who maintained a steady disconcerting tremor but it didn't take long to open along the jaw and expose the area of broken bone. The .22 bullet lay misshapen where it had come to rest between the two sections of shattered mandible. Mending broken bones in circumstances such as this is basic carpentry – furniture repair on living tissue. Placing the two pieces of jawbone together, I fixed them by means of an oblong vitallium metal plate attached to the bone with vitallium screws, three on each side of the break, that I tightened up using a sterilised stainless steel screwdriver. The constantly dithering sea-lion made correct precisioning of the first screw on each side an intricate and laborious business, but eventually I finished it and then because the break had been at a very acute angle I strapped stainless steel wire thread round the jawbone for extra support. I was working in the sea-lion house that had been washed down with disinfectant – there was no posh veterinary hospital or operating theatre at Cleethorpes like the one at London or Madrid Zoos. All the instruments had been sterilised and were part of the orthopaedic kit I brought with me from Flamingo Park. After the bones had been joined I had sprayed the wound with antibiotic powder before closing up first with catgut and finally with strong nylon for the skin. Knowing well the ease with which sea-lion wounds or even hypodermic injections could become infected, so infested with bacteria are their skins, I had given the unconscious sea-lion a final massive dose of broad spectrum antibiotic into his buttocks.

After the operation the animal had taken its time about waking up. The phencyclidine cleared slowly from its system and it wasn't alert and moving around for over one and a half days. But it didn't look good. The swelling of the face increased rather than diminished, the operation wound began to ooze an unpleasant-smelling liquid and the sea-lion developed a high fever. More antibiotics, different ones, were pumped in. I removed a couple of stitches from the jaw to improve drainage. To no avail – the animal's condition went rapidly down hill and I soon found the reason in the report that came from the lab after they'd examined a swab of that smelly liquid. It was loaded with a vicious fast-multiplying germ – the sort that loves to live in damp places like flower vases (you've almost certainly got some right now in that bunch of chrysanthemums on the window-sill) and of course just about everywhere on or in a sea-lion. It was the sort of bug that sometimes contaminates hospital wards leading to their temporary closure and has been known, with devastating results, to sneak into bottles of saline used in operating theatres. It had bedevilled the early heart transplant operations by delighting in invading a body whose resistance had been reduced by the use of drugs given to control rejection of a new heart. Its name was Pseudomonas – it was to prove to be one of my greatest adversaries in later years when wrestling with the diseases of aquatic mammals and it was totally resistant to all the antibiotics that had been discovered up to that time. One week after the operation the sea-lion had died from overwhelming blood poisoning due to the Pseudomonas microbe. My first open repair of fractured sea-lion bones left me depressed and apprehensive about any sort of radical surgical intervention in this species.

Before leaving for Majorca I had asked Robert to make

arrangements with one of the small animal veterinary clinics in Palma for an X-ray machine to be available when I arrived. That was how we came to be shooing a sea-lion full of valium along the pavement in the warm evening. After dashing from the airport to Marineland I had seen at once that Nina's jaw was probably fractured. I had given her the tranquilliser and then we took her by van into the city. A sensible and thoughtful animal, Nina hauled herself along from the place where we parked as close as possible to the clinic, with Robert and me bringing up the rear and Marcus beside her carrying an oblong sheet of plywood to block her path just in case she fancied making a dash into 'Tito's' nightclub to see how the showgirls were coming along. The Spanish vet had everything ready for us including a complete set of orthopaedic instruments should I require them. Nina looked round his surgery and with her twisted mouth gave the impression of a child ruefully surveying the dentist's torture chamber. To X-ray her I needed to have her head held still on the film plates. The valium was fine for making her dreamy but something else was required to knock her out for a few minutes. Marcus brought a nylon net from the van. We dropped it over her and pinned her gently to the surgery floor. Through the mesh I injected a small dose of quick-acting ketamine. All the time I was thinking of the Cleethorpes sea-lion and its sad end. Nowadays we have antibiotics that can get to grips with Pseudomonas but the possibility of post-operative infection by resistant water-loving bacteria still threatened. Please God let the radiograph show a nice straightforward dislocation only! Push, twist, PUSH! Click. It would be done. Nothing more needed but a few days of aspirin for Nina. And instead of two or three hours surgery we could drive out to Genova for spicy snails and a bottle of Muga wine.

Of course, it didn't turn out like that. The radiograph showed Nina's lower jaw to resemble a higgledy-piggledy jumble of firewood. Billy's head butt had smashed the bone into a multiple fracture with the accent on multiple. Dismayed, I explained the situation to Robert. Steel pins, clips, vitallium plates, nails and wire were not going to be any help here. The jaw had virtually disintegrated – opening up on to that chaos of shards and splinters would be an utter waste of time. My friend was aghast. He too had hoped for a dislocation but guesssed an operation would be needed. Together we had struggled long hours and nursed touch-and-go cases in diseased marine mammals many times in the past. What Robert hadn't contemplated was me saying, 'There's nothing to be done!'

Euthanasia was something we'd never done or even talked about before. We'd always tried everything and anything with Marineland's seals, sea-lions, dolphins – and its parrots, alligators and coypu.

'Are you sure there's nothing?' he muttered. 'You mean it's either letting her starve to death, unable to eat, or putting her down?'

I looked down at the sleeping sea-lion stretched out on the surgery floor, stirring now as the ketamine wore off. 'That's about it,' I replied glumly. 'There's no way I can fix that idiot's jigsaw! Doing nothing . . .' Nothing. Doing nothing for fractures. Nina opened a liquid brown eye and looked lugubriously up at us. Suppose I did nothing, *could do* nothing in a physical, surgical sense and just nursed her? Gave her vitamins, minerals, tissue-building hormones (the sort Olympic athletes aren't supposed to use) and just waited? But how would she obtain food through that mangled mouth? Could she even suck up even enough water to quench her thirst? I'd seen lots of wild birds with old fractures that had healed satisfactorily without benefit of veterinarians but just a nod and a wink from Mother Nature, who must have kept predators away until the limb was functioning again. There are numerous fossils of sabre-tooth tigers, deer and giant sloths with solid calluses of new bone that had formed round fractured legs and skulls. Most impressive of all, I remembered the experiment done in South Africa years before with cattle that had broken their legs. Such injuries were considered surgically irreparable and even today cattle and horses with fractures of major limb bones are normally killed. The South African cattle, however, were simply turned out to fend for themselves on a vast area of grassland where there was plenty of grazing and water year round. After two years the survivors were rounded up and examined. Amazingly a high proportion were alive and walking, albeit not always with a perfect gait, on healed limbs. Time and rest of the injured limb (four-legged animals have an advantage in still being able to get around on three) had been the only treatment.

But the jaw of a sea-lion might be quite another thing from the legs of wild birds and cattle. And I had never heard of a sea-lion, modern or fossilised, having been found with a naturally healed broken jaw. Nevertheless.

'I'll tell you what,' I said to Robert. '*If* and it's a big if, we can get water and enough food to keep body and soul into her somehow – it would be worth a try giving the Turkish Treatment.'

'Turkish Treatment?'

'Doing nowt as they say in Lancashire – apart from giving her stuff to promote bone healing.'

'How do you propose to get nourishment into her?'

'Let's get her loaded into the van, take her back to Marineland and then give me two things. The old sea-lion examination cage and Pauline.'

We slipped the net under the still drowsy sea-lion and carried her out to the delight of one German holidaymaker in the street outside who, on seeing our 'catch' as we went by, shouted to his wife, 'See Gretchen, I told you there are still fish in the Mediterranean. Look, the local fishermen are coming home with a big one tonight!' The 'big one' obligingly waved a sleepy flipper at him to prove it.

Pauline Johann, an ever cheerful Yorkshire girl and an

accomplished dolphin and sea-lion handler in her own right, is married to Marcus, Marineland's sea-lion trainer. I had observed her relaxed and sensitive way with animals on many occasions, not least in the successful bringing up on the bottle of 'Jock', a Californian sea-lion pup. She had coaxed and coddled Jock through the colics and collywobbles of infancy, finely tuned his milkless 'milk' formula of blended herring, oil and water and encouraged him through the often tricky weaning period where some awkward individuals need force-feeding of whole fish for weeks on end before they get the idea that they are supposed to be the 'lions of the sea' – underwater eagles who effortlessly and elegantly swoop down on shoals of fish and squid and gobble as much as 15 kilos of live food a day. Pauline was also a dab hand at coaxing dolphins who can be rather conservative and fixed in their eating ways, insisting on a monotonous diet of nothing but herring, herring, herring day in day out, to accept a broader healthier diet of various kinds of fish – mackerel, capelin, sprat, cuttlefish and whiting. She had, in short, the knack that some grandmothers have in getting their grandchildren to eat their greens. I decided to put Nina into a sea-lion treatment cage, a specially built device that looks like a giant toast-rack and keep her there for a considerable time – possibly weeks. In the cage we could handle her easily at all times, hose her down to keep her skin in good condition and perhaps, perhaps Pauline could tease tiny scraps of fish flesh into the ravaged mouth.

Back at the Marineland, Nina was installed in the cage and after a shot of vitamins and painkillers left to sleep off the residue of the valium. Next day I explained to Pauline exactly what we wanted her to try to achieve. To get even the smallest quantities of liquid, the merest milligram of fish on to Nina's tongue – without touching the jaws or pushing the animal. To give the sea-lion the idea of sucking and slurping nourishment in. Robert took Pauline off all her other duties so that she could concentrate solely on the task. The

Yorkshire girl armed herself with a dish of soft herring fillets and a kettle full of water with a rubber spout and set to work with enthusiasm. By the end of the first day she had got precisely nowhere with Nina. Her gentle words of encouragement, proffered titbits and trickles of cool water were all rejected with polite indifference. The head was turned away from the fish, the water was allowed to run off the tip of the chin. But at least she let Pauline bring her fingers close to her mouth without threatening her. When Robert or I or anyone else tried our hand at wooing her acceptance of the morsels we were roared at, lunged at and occasionally, even with her broken jaw, snapped at. With the weather hot I was concerned that Nina might become seriously dehydrated, so by swinging in the movable bars of her treatment cage and gently but firmly holding her still I gave her fluids. While she roared and honked indignantly and rolled her eyes in surprise at the front end, I pumped half a gallon of glucose saline in at the back end through an enema tube.

The next day dawned bright and cheerful in more senses than one. When I arrived at the Marineland I was greeted with the news that Nina had let Pauline place an inch-long sliver of mackerel on the extreme tip of her tongue. Painfully, awkwardly and without aid of normal jaw movements she had got the bit of fish to the back of her mouth somehow and swallowed it. And what was even better, she was looking for more! I went to watch. Pauline was sitting on a stool at the front end of the treatment cage intently watching the female sea-lion whose nose was just a few inches away from her on the other side of the metal bars. It was an eyeball to eyeball business that gave the impression of some sort of intimate conversation – a sea-lion's psychiatrist's couch or a zoological confessional with the girl murmuring and the animal listening and snuffling. Nina was paying attention all right but you could see she was torn between the hunger and the heavy ache in her mouth. There was the gleaming grey morsel held patiently and steadily in the fingers that almost touched her nose. Nina looked at the fingers and then at Pauline. Ah, but she knew too well the mysterious new agony of opening the mouth – better to resist the unbearable temptation. The sea-lion looked away – almost as if embarrassed by Pauline's unblinking gaze. The smell of mackerel was maddening to the sensitive nose – that certainly hadn't been broken. After a second or two, Nina looked again at Pauline and then at those tantalising fingers. Perhaps . . . perhaps if by wriggling the tongue just a little bit, by letting the raging jaw droop first ever so slowly, ever so slightly and then raising the head . . . The fingers came closer. The fish – ah, the taste of that Cornish mackerel – it was as fresh as the moment it had been hauled in off the Scillies. Hey! . . . The fingers had pushed the fish actually into contact with the tongue – so very slowly. Yes, it was just possible to take it. And . . . swallow! A flash of pain – but the taste! The fingers again – a new smell. What was this? – oh, this should help the fish to slip along! The girl had lubricated the next piece in heavenly cod liver oil. The second swallow was just that little bit easier.

It took all morning but by lunchtime Pauline had got a whole herring minus its fins, head, bones and guts, piece by piece into Nina. And the sea-lion had learned to swallow water from the slowly trickling kettle. By nightfall the princely total of two fish – 300 grams of sustenance – had been achieved. Not much but enough to make me feel we were in with more than a fighting chance. As it turned out that feeling was justified. The following day Pauline got Nina to swallow 500 grams of fish and with slightly less effort. The sea-lion also sucked water from a running hosepipe held over her head although she couldn't manage to drink from the bowl. From then on steady progress was made by the pair until after ten days Pauline was slipping 8 kilos of herring and mackerel pieces, some loaded with vitamins and the hormone tablets, into the sea-lion and getting it down in less than half an hour. Nina's bodily condition improved and little by little she opened and moved her mouth more, although there was a prominent displacement of the lower jaw to the left which resulted in her fang tooth on that side lying outside the upper lip.

'That's the least of our worries,' I told Robert, as we watched the sea-lion leave the treatment cage at the end of two weeks when I judged she was fit to go back to more normal quarters, but not in the same pool as brutal Billy. 'If the tooth causes any embarrassment in that position I'll take it out or file down and fill it – but not until we've given many more weeks for that jaw to sort itself out.' Somehow the jumbled pieces of bone in the jaw were being bound together by deposits of soft new bone that would steadily harden. The remarkable healing power of a wild animal – far greater than that of domesticated creatures including Homo sapiens – was being demonstrated to us. Two months after the accident Nina was back to normal except for her side-slipped mouth. She could open her jaws, chew and swallow food as efficiently as ever and cavorted on land and in the water with her fellows without any sign of discomfort. Doing nothing had certainly been the right treatment in Nina's case and a happy bi-product was the close friendship that had been sealed between the big animal and the girl who had brought her through, literally by the skin of her teeth. If you go to the Marineland at Palma Nova watch out for the sea-lion with the twisted and toothy grin – that's Nina.

In 1984, I had the opportunity to use the same therapy of masterly inactivity in another sea-lion, this time a Patagonian female belonging to my Swiss circus friend, Roberto Gasser. As in Nina's case she had been severely wounded by a massive male who had snapped at her and inflicted multiple fractures of the lower *and* upper jaw. By a rare quirk of fate his snapping jaws had caught her with her mouth open and one of his long fang teeth had broken through the roof of the mouth into the nasal passageways. I had never seen that sort of injury in a sea-lion before. The accident happened while Gasser and his animals were performing at the La Scala Club in Madrid. Again on this occasion I had the ideal nurse and helpmate on hand to coax the sea-lion slowly to eat – my good friend Liliana Monsalve, the vet at Madrid Zoo. The Gasser animal was moved to the sea-lion house at the Zoo de la Casa de Campo and put into a 'private ward' with its own personal pool. Because the fractures, unlike those in Nina's case, were compound as well as multiple due to the tooth penetration, there was grave risk of infection leading perhaps to osteomyelitis and septicaemia. Again we concentrated on providing the necessary vitamins, minerals, painkillers and tissue building hormones and also gave thrice daily doses of the antibiotic gentamicin to ward off Pseudomonas and his pals. Apart from that the main thrust of the nursing was for Liliana to gain the confidence of the animal and to 'love' it into taking bites of fish. The female sea-lion was a tough nut. So great was the damage to the jaw that the poor creature didn't accept a single piece of food for two and a half weeks. During that period it lost weight rapidly and became a leathery bag of bones. But it did take water on board – it liked being sprayed in the face and mouth with a slow running hosepipe although it rarely went for a dip in its pool. I began to wonder if my 'Turkish Treatment' was going to end up starving the animal to death. Then at last, on the eighteenth day, Liliana's patience was rewarded. The sea-lion took its first scrap of mackerel. From then on it progressed just like Nina had, though I kept it at the zoo for observation for a further five weeks until it was plump and glossy and catching whole mackerel thrown to it, turning them adroitly by a toss of the head and swallowing them always head first as sea-lions do. And in this case the animal recovered without any apparent distortion of the mouth or jaws.

I'm not making a plea for a *laissez-faire* approach to animal fractures in all this. Usually surgical intervention is essential and to be embarked upon without delay, but in the special conditions of virtually inoperable fractures in the head of a marine animal such as a sea-lion one should never lose hope and remember to say one's prayers – they tend to be rewarded.

2 A Day in the Oasis

'It must be fascinating travelling all over the world to look at every kind of unusual animal – what a great job!' How many times have I heard that. My standard reply about greener grass is more than a glib attempt at modesty. I write at this moment at the end of another long day in the Arabian desert near the Buraimi Oasis, standing in at the Al Ain Zoo for my assistant Chris Furley who has gone on leave. I am back doing the nitty-gritty of exotic animal work as the zoo's house surgeon. There are echoes of the days long ago at Flamingo Park in Yorkshire and Belle Vue in Manchester, even of general practice as a green young vet on Milnrow Road, Rochdale – but against a backcloth that is a blend of the old feudal Thousand and One Nights and the harsh modern Arabia of OPEC, militant Islam and Pepsi-Cola cans littering the highways, where camels nap at night seeking the warmth retained by the asphalt and providing lethal traffic hazards for the latter-day caravans of Mercedes and Toyotas.

It is important to utilise the best of the day, the few hours after dawn and at sunset, to the full – at these times the air is cool and silky and the sky is like mother of pearl seen through gauze. My limbs, that move as if through treacle in the furnace heat between 9 and 4 pm, work normally then. But the cool time of the day is when I can give anaesthetics to patients requiring surgery in the vast sandy paddocks that are simply wire-fenced tracts of desert. To operate, except in an absolute emergency, in the heat of the day would be foolhardy. An unconscious animal, the heat-regulating centres in its brain dormant under the effect of the soporific drugs, can overheat and literally cook its vital organs. Snakes and other reptiles that need the beneficial effects of solar ultraviolet light must be put out for remedial sunbaths only up till 9 or 9.30 am. After that even the saw-scaled vipers, native to this arid land, run the risk of being grilled to death by the white heat. So high is the temperature during much of the year that the very flies cannot survive except in deep shade and mosquito larvae are destroyed by the warmth of the water in the drinking water tanks. Only the blood-sucking ticks that can shelter in the sand and in the fur on the skin of their hosts manage to survive and spread the infectious diseases that they carry in their mouth-parts to deer, antelope and other stock. So a typical day begins at first light with the muezzin's call from the mosque that stands a mile away from my window beneath the range of mountains that jut abruptly and lopsided without attendant foothills out of the desert floor. Rich red tea, a mush of purple brown beans, some pickled olives and a small disc of Arab bread form my breakfast and then I drive the ten miles to the zoo in the bone-jarring four-wheel drive Daihatsu.

Al Ain Zoo is unique – a desert animal park conceived and brought into being by one man, Otto Bulart, an Austrian engineer with a deep love of animals but no formal zoological training. Covering 450 hectares of mainly flat and stony desert with a paucity of very brackish water far beneath the sand, it has been painstakingly brought alive over fifteen years with groves of low trees, bushes, stretches of grass, roads and air-conditioned buildings. There are penguins, gazelles, colobus monkeys, tigers and gorillas here – mammals and birds from every continent. In the great sandy paddocks at the furthest extremes of the zoo where visitors rarely go (it is too far to walk in the heat), all manner of hoofed stock live in conditions that for some species such as oryx and gazelle are close to natural. There have been failures – the red deer of Europe are plagued by parasites that invade their blood cells and which Chris and I think, but can't yet prove, are carried by ticks. African bongo, forest animals, have hated the desert conditions of Arabia and have done badly while cheetah, lovers of long grass for moments of privacy, decline to breed among the naked low dunes of their enclosure. But as well as caring for its own inhabitants, the zoo also perforce provides a thousand other services for the people and animals of the Abu Dhabi Emirate. The myriad Bedou sheikhs of the region feel free to drop in at any time of day or night with falcons or gazelles that have problems to obtain medicines gratis (supplying a man with enough mite spray for fifty falcons or antibiotic cream for his camel makes a significant hole in our meagre drug budget); the local hospital sends a man each Sunday morning for blood we draw from a group of sheep in order that they may prepare blood agar plates for their bacteriological department; the police bring their newly arrived German shepherd dogs, most of them more homesick for Europe and stunned by desert life than clinically ill; and the local nomads happily cut our fences to let in their goats and camels to graze and forage in our paddocks. To the zoo come doctors seeking advice on exotic diseases, Arabs demanding guinea pigs and rabbits for their falcons, oil men's wives wanting rabies shots for dogs that will never return to England, sly sellers of bad hay and grossly overpriced and untested medicines from India and Pakistan, animal dealers from all over the world greedy for Arab gold, nobles with unwanted gifts of eagles, ostriches or tigers that they drop off unannounced at our gate, and Afghani labourers with sores that they wish the English animal doctor to treat, having already had bad experiences with the Syrian or Egyptian doctors in the town.

At 7 o'clock I begin my first tour of the day – driving round the zoo to shake hands with everyone and see whether there have been any births, deaths or alarums during the night. The 150 workers in the zoo are a mixture of Indians, Pakistanis, Afghanis, Iranis and Baluchis. In a sense they are all rich men. Although paid somewhat less than their European counterparts, they earn more in a month here than they would in a year in their home villages. Most have built fine houses back home with the wealth they send back through the money changers, and on their visits to their families every couple of years they are feted as the Jasons of their societies. The formal handshaking must take an hour's time in all spread over the morning. Everyone does it. So with 150 people doing it 365 days a year that means there's around 325 weeks of handshaking in the Al Ain Zoo per annum! To check the animals far away in the shining sand and white light of the paddocks I use binoculars. A pair of hoopoes, King Solomon's messengers according to the Koran, swoop across the sky. One individual in the gemsbok enclosure stands apart from the rest, its head down as if daydreaming. The rest of the herd stand alert watching me and interrupting their breakfast of alfalfa as I stop the jeep and go over to stand at the fence. The binoculars reveal a dark stain and tomato-sized bubble on the single gemsbok's flank. It is a male and has been gored by a rival. The bubble implies that the horn has penetrated the abdomen. A jury line of eight Egyptian vultures sit impassively on the top of the fencing watching the stricken animal with airs of great patience. I call the Indian gemsbok keeper – he comes over and salutes with military precision (he was trained in the British army) and I send him for the curator and two more men. When he trots off I return to the jeep to prepare for emergency surgery. The coolbox in the jeep runs off the vehicle's dashboard cigar lighter and struggles to keep a basic supply of key drugs from being vitiated by the climate. In there also are sterilised packs of instruments – nothing fancy, but enough to cut, staunch and stitch the majority of the zoo's battlefield casualties. I fill an aluminium flying syringe with a teaspoonful of etorphine anaesthetic and load it into the rifle.

With a bit of luck I should be able to walk to within

20 yards of the gemsbok before it moves off – the distance is critical for I have to select a blank cartridge of the appropriate power to throw the syringe at the target animal. Too high a power, too short a distance and the whole projectile, needle barrel and plastic flight, can blast its way into the body inflicting more damage than a bullet. Too low powered a cartridge and the syringe will cruise down to land in the sand and leave me with egg on my face, feeling like one of those circus clowns whose blunderbuss fires a little flag bearing the word 'BANG'. I select a blue-coloured cartridge and slip it into the breach behind the syringe. The gemsbok turns its head without raising it as I open the gate of the enclosure and walk, not directly towards it – that would be very provocative – but along a line that would take me past it. I watch it out of the corner of my eye and pretend it is the last animal on earth that I am concerned with. A hundred yards. Fifty. Twenty-five. I stop. The handsome grey antelope from the Kalahari desert with its black and white harlequin's face and swordlike backward-sloping horns still hasn't moved. The ominous dark stain on its side is blood all right and the bubble is a handful of glistening abdominal tissue. For the first time I turn to face the animal squarely, slowly raise the rifle, feel a hopeful fly that has come along on spec buzzing round my ear (can't risk flicking at it now), take aim and squeeze the trigger. With a sharp crack the gun fires and the gemsbok springs away. But not quick enough. Held by a tiny barb on the needle tip, the syringe goes with it, having discharged its contents on impact into the rounded haunch muscle and twinkling like a bolt of silver in the morning light. The wounded gemsbok runs 100 yards, stops, half turns to watch me and begins to make chewing movements with its mouth. The first etorphine has reached the brain. The animal now begins to walk again but this time at a prissy, high-stepping trot. Noticing the abnormal gait of their fellow, some of the other gemsbok now begin to move towards it to investigate and very likely attack it. Unusual

behaviour is punished in herds such as these. I run, sweat stinging my eyes, towards the advancing group and wave my arms. They sheer away. The keeper is back with two Afghani keepers from nearby paddocks. The slowly trotting gemsbok suddenly knuckles at the knees, goes down on to its brisket and then weakly lowers its hind quarters.

'*La*, *la* – don't go up to it yet!' I shout to the keepers. The drug must take a firm hold. I remember a German fellow who was a bit too impatient in rushing up to a Beisa oryx (a close relative of the gemsbok and armed with equally lethal horns) after it had been darted with anaesthetic. When he reached it, the still half-conscious animal tried to get to its feet and in doing so threw back its head violently impaling the keeper through the groin. When I got up to him he'd already lost about a pint of blood through the torn femoral artery which was literally hanging out of the gaping hole in his trousers. His unwary and precipitate approach to a dangerous animal in a state where the world must be spinning furiously and where we know (if etorphine is used) that sensitivity to sound is actually *increased*, cost me a rather natty safari jacket that I had to rip to pieces on the spot to make a tourniquet. When I am satisfied that the gemsbok is dead to the world, except as I say perhaps for its sense of hearing, I give the signal and we all move in. I clean my hands quickly using the penlike dispenser of antiseptic soapy liquid, actually manufactured for undertakers, which I carry in my breast pocket. Next I test the eye reflexes, the position of the tongue, the breathing (slow and depressed) and the heart. Fine – now for the wound. The hole is indeed a penetration of the skin, all muscle layers and the peritoneum. The bubble I saw through the binoculars is a ball of blood smeared omentum, the lace-like tissue that strings the intestines together. Cautiously I spread the ball of tissue looking for major blood vessels or any contained loops of bowel. There are none. My passenger fly disembarks from my head and without a word of thanks makes for the fortuitous banquet. The vultures on the nearby fence shuffle their feet and crane their necks expectantly – they've moved along to be as close as possible to the action and look like gowned but rather wizened undergraduate medical students attending a surgery demonstration. I open my surgery pack and use the spread palms of one of the Afghanis covered with a square of sterile green drape as an instrument trolley. There is sand adhering to some of the protruding tissue – no time to waste and, sand being impossible to wash off, I cut that portion away.

'*Batil kresha*' (I *think* that means 'open bottle' in the pigeon Arabic that is the lingua franca around here) I say, and at least the other Afghani seems to understand as I gesticulate. He takes the top off a bottle of saline solution. I point to the wound and he pours some over the exposed tissues. The liquid runs down over the belly and disappears into the sand. I point to my hair – he grins and pours the remainder of the bottle in a delicious stream on to my sizzling head. Cooler for a moment, I pack the omentum back into the abdomen and then extend the horn wound a little with a scalpel to get a better look inside. I can see no signs of internal bleeding or other damage. The curator has arrived and I ask him to squirt three tubes of penicillin/streptomycin udder cream, normally used for treating mastitis in cattle, into the hole in the abdomen without touching the wound. That done, I start stitching – bringing together the layers of peritoneum and muscle with triple knotted separate sutures of heavy gauge catgut. More udder antibiotic is then applied to the row of stitches by the curator. My knees have got cramp through kneeling in the baking sand. With the help of needle holders I punch holes in the tough skin and draw the wound finely together with vicryl that will dissolve in time. The operation wound is finally sprayed with a maggot-deterrent sulphonamide powder and the operation is over. The gemsbok's breathing and circulation are now very depressed due to the effect of etorphine and the mouth and tongue are violet coloured. No matter – the antidote injection will quickly sort that out. The instruments are gathered together and I tell the men to stand back. Fifteen seconds after I have completed a small intravenous injection into the gemsbok's jugular, the animal suddenly gives a deep breath, snorts and springs to its feet. With barely a wobble it walks sedately away to join the rest of the herd. As I make my way back to the jeep I note that the vultures have disappeared.

'*Der-herr*, *der-herr*, gentlemen,' I thank the keepers. There is more handshaking before I drive off to continue my morning tour. It is 8.35 am and the first visitors are arriving. I must go now to the bear house to check on a worrying case of a bear cub that is passing large quantities of pure blood in the urine. I suspect a bladder polyp but can't operate until the animal is stronger. Twice a day I grab the cub with a rope loop on the end of a pole and give him his injections and an infusion of glucose saline. At the bear house a fat, sullen-faced Arab in a red doughnut-like turban and sandy coloured dish-dasha is throwing stones at the brown bears and ignoring the protests of a young Keralan keeper. I stop the jeep and weigh up the situation. By his dress he is definitely an Omani and not a sheikh. Sheikhs, if they wish, *can* throw stones at bears or demand that the nearest keeper open a cage so that they can take home with them some pretty bird they fancy or one which might prove to be good sport for their falcons. Sheikhs can poke animals with sticks, pick flowers, drive their Mercedes round the parts of the zoo where pedestrians only are permitted or give lighted cigarettes to the monkeys. Remonstrate with a First Division sheikh and his armed guards will soon see you off. An unattended Second Division sheikh will, if you spoil his fun, perhaps make life difficult by calling the police or complaining to the Ruler. And sheikhs, of course, when it comes to an argument, are always right.

'Stop throwing stones,' I say walking up to the Omani wagging a finger. He ignores me and searches around his feet for another missile. 'Stop at once!' – would that I had Chris's passable command of Arabic! The sullen face develops a glare behind the black beard and black bushy eyebrows. 'Stop . . . or . . . or Sheikh Zayd, Sheikh Zayd!' I bellow the name of the Ruler of the Emirates. It is the best I can think of. The Omani holds his arm in mid throw and drops the stone. 'Sheikh Zayd,' I repeat fiercely spitting the words out. Under the impression that His Highness is either about to appear or owns the bears or that I am a royal councillor, the Omani scowls and strides off muttering what I take to be curses. I decide that the Sheikh Zayd mantra will be used in future on all stone-throwing cases.

'Good lad,' I say to the keeper, 'you did your best.' The Arabs generally ignore the remonstrations of Asian foreigners, for whom they have a general disdain, in such situations.

'He was also stoning the monkeys sir, and the wolves,' answers the keeper. The palm-frond roof of the wolves' day shelter is always threatening to collapse as it sags under the weight of stones and rocks thrown by visitors at the poor animals. Thank God their aim is so poor, probably because of their robes and the fact that they don't play cricket. 'Are you a Moslem?' I ask the boy.

'No sir – Mar Thoma Christian from Kerala.'

'You know why they stone bears?'

'No sir.'

'Because it is said Allah sentenced certain sinful humans to be changed into pigs and monkeys. As for bears they consider them to be pigs – with hair.'

I finish the morning tour and go back to the veterinary clinic and the relief of its air-conditioned coolnesss. Philip, the lab technician, gives me the results of yesterday's blood samples of a young gibbon that is losing weight and continually sleeping – it has leukaemia. I must decide quickly whether to try one of the new chemical agents used on a similar condition in humans.

'There is a messenger waiting for you in the office from Sheikh Hussain.' Philip interrupts my thoughts. 'He says it is important.' I groan loudly. Important probably means that I am to go at once on a journey lasting three or four hours by car and then maybe by boat to see an animal that first fell ill or retained its placenta after giving birth, or that the Sheikh decided that he didn't want any more and it should be somehow caught and brought to the zoo, a week ago. So much for my plans to deal with the Laristan sheep that needs examining later in the morning. I walk along to the main administration block and after more 'pressing the flesh' as the Americans say, get a tiny cup of Turkish coffee and a glass of iced water while an interpreter sits with Sheikh Hussain's man and me.

'Three things, doctor,' says the interpreter. 'Firstly, the Sheikh sends his greetings and says he hopes you will be able to join him hunting in Pakistan this winter.' No chance of that. Obsessively security minded, the Gulf Sheikhs never let anyone except their closest circle know when or where they will be at any given moment. They pop at random from palace to palace with the unpredictability of nuclear particles. Perhaps the call to go falconing would come – but it would be literally ten minutes before he boarded his private jet. Not much good with me in England and permanently needing a desk diary with eight days to the week.

'Secondly,' he continues, 'great news. His Highness is the proud breeder of the first Houbara bustards in the Gulf. Four eggs hatched yesterday at the farm at Zaniq. He thanks you for your advice on the feeding of the Houbara and asks that you inform the World Wildlife Fund, London Zoo and San Diego Zoo.'

'Wonderful. Please convey my congratulations,' I reply. And think 'bull dust'. I was at the Zaniq farm a week ago. There wasn't a sign or mention of any reproductive activity let alone egg-laying Houbara, the birds so prized by the Bedou. All the Sheikhs would give their eye teeth to be the first to breed these nervous and rather unimpressive birds in captivity. The feeding recommendations I'd given were those used in the Tel Aviv University Zoo in Israel (or Occupied Palestine as the Sheikhs would have it) where breeding has been achieved. I've no doubt the Sheikh is in possession of four new hatched Houbara chicks, nor have I any doubt as to where they've come from. On the grapevine I've heard that several nobles have imported hopefully fertile eggs taken from nests in the Indian subcontinent. They've had them incubated like hens' eggs and now here's the first one claiming it was all his own work.

'Thirdly,' the interpreter says, 'His Highness asks for some tiger meat.' Now that is a new one.

'Tiger meat?' I ask. 'We feed nothing special to the big cats here at the Zoo. Old horses, occasionally a camel, good quality beef – most is bought in from the market. Some we slaughter here.' Much as I detest killing animals it is essential that the vet or one of the European curators of the zoo shoot any live animals brought to the zoo for feeding – if we don't our Moslem keepers will cut their throats in the time-honoured Islamic way.

'Can't His Highness buy meat for some reason?' The Sheikh's man converses in rapid Arabic with my interpreter.

'No doctor, you don't understand. His Highness wants tiger meat. Meat *from* not *for* the tiger.'

'You mean he wants to eat tiger meat?' The Bedous of this region were accustomed to much hunger in the past and ate anything that came their way. Old Salem the gatekeeper asked me for hyena brain last week to strengthen his thinking capacity. I've read in the *Dictionnaire Des Sciences Medicales* of a porter at the Jardin des Plantes in Paris who in the nineteenth century ate the body of a lion that had died of disease in the menagerie, and more recently of lion, tiger and other exotic animal flesh being sold at high prices for human consumption both in Belgium and West Germany.

'Yes, one of his sons is getting married next week and there will be eight days of feasting. Thousands of guests. For his very special guests he wants something special.'

'Sorry, we have no dead tigers.' Tigers thrive happily at Al Ain.

'But you can kill one surely doctor.'

'No we can't.' The Sheikh's messenger, a handsome toothbrush-moustached Bedou in immaculate white robes, frowns and stares hard at me when the interpreter smiling rather obsequiously puts it to him.

'But you have many tigers here. His Highness requires one.'

'I am sorry but no we can't. Anyway the tigers are not well at present.'

'They are ill?'

'Well no.' Here I go with the terminological inexactitudes again. 'Not exactly – but as you know I am consultant here and I have detected during my specialised examination that our tigers have got a sterility problem.'

'You mean they cannot breed?'

'Exactly.' Let's hope he doesn't hear about the cubs we had last year. 'And the complaint is spreading.'

'Spreading?'

'It moves from one tiger to another. It came to them from rats we think. And it can travel on.' Let's hope he swallows this. 'To anyone who eats the flesh – like an infection, like food poisoning. Contagious impotency!!' The Sheikh's man is fascinated. His master has had a narrow escape.

'Oh, thank you doctor – your advice is most welcome. Now perhaps you have something else – elephant, rhinoceros?' Dismayed, I realise that I am by no means out of the wood. Sipping my iced water clears the brain.

After a few minutes silence I say, 'There is one thing I can do for His Highness – but this is very rare, a one-off, never-to-be-repeated speciality.' Both men bend towards me wide-eyed. 'I can let His Highness have,' I continue, 'the meat of a polar bear.'

'The Ice Bear? I didn't know we had any such animals here at Al Ain.'

'We haven't – this meat comes from an animal that I shot a week ago just before coming here. It will be in prime condition now. There will be just enough for His Highness and two or three of his closest friends.' A crescent moon of shining white teeth rises as a smile splits the messenger's face.

'Doctor, you are a good fellow. That will please His Highness.' Handshakes all round. I stand up.

'One moment,' I say, 'I will go to my laboratory to get it.' I walk back to the clinic as fast as the heat will allow, collect my keys and go over to Chris's bungalow. In the refrigerator there is a full Chateaubriand that cost me sixty dirhams at Choithrams Grocery. Doused quickly in Drakkar after-shave lotion before I wrap it in an old copy of the *Khaleej Times*, it should have an interesting toothsome, not to say polar bear flavour. Who's to say different out here?

The messenger and my dinners for the next three days gone, I go for lunch and then the afternoon siesta which lasts until three – stretched out on the couch in the bungalow, a Mozart tape turned up to full volume to drown the din of the cicadas that abound in the creepers outside on the veranda.

Mid-afternoon and the heat presses down on the zoo like an eiderdown. The keepers are sitting or sprawling in small groups in the shade of bushes. All the animals are torpid and noiseless at this time of day. Nothing ever happens between three and four – time to get paperwork done, to sort out pickled pathological specimens to take back to England for specialised examination and to clean the dart gun and syringes. It begins to cool slightly after four and as I look out of the clinic window I see a European girl in a sleeveless batik blouse and tennis shorts walking past the gibbon cages with a camera slung over her shoulder. Her skin is pink with the first phase of sunburn – obviously a recent arrival, a nurse at the Tawam Hospital or the wife of some oil technician out on a short visit and, with little enough to do around here, looking forward to a pleasant wander for an hour or so among the animals in what is surely the greenest and shadiest place for many miles around. To me it is an emergency. In a society like this, largely composed of expatriot males separated from their womenfolk often for years at a time and most of whom come from cultures where females cover most of their bodies when in public, such a young lady can be too much. In Wigan or Washington her attire would be entirely appropriate on a scorching summer's day and would certainly not be considered provocative or daring. But here unpleasant things have happened, even in the zoo. Some of our own staff might flip if she goes awandering deep into the gardens. I dash out and call her. It is a matter that has to be handled delicately but very firmly. The girl turns out indeed to be an Irish nurse who arrived only a week ago at the hospital.

'Sleeves, slacks or a mid-length skirt and a companion – don't leave home without them,' I tell her and escort her back to her car outside the main gate.

At 5 o'clock I judge it is cool enough to deal with the Laristan sheep. A young ram, it has been staggering in anti-clockwise circles round the paddock with its head tilted to the left. The keepers have at last managed to catch the still fleet-foot animal with nets and taken it up to one of the cool quarantine rooms at the top of the zoo. With three men holding the powerfully built ram down I examine it. It is in fine bodily condition and the stomach is full of newly eaten food. Through my opthalmoscope I peer deep into the dark eyes. The right pupil, letter-box shaped as in many species that need to scan a wide arc of the horizon while their heads are down grazing in case predators should appear, is much more dilated than the left. What is more, when I bring the retina at the back of the eye sharply into focus, the disc that indicates where the optic nerve linking the eye to the brain begins is fuzzy and blurred. The disc must be raised and puffy. While one of the keepers holds the head upright I go over every inch of the ram's skull probing through the harsh hair with the tips of my fingers. The head is hard and dusty but after a while I detect a spot about the size of a five pence piece on the left side directly above the eye where the bone yields to my pressure. Soft bone. That clinches it. Shades of the Pennine Hills, the rain drizzling interminably on flocks of sooty Lonk sheep above Littleborough where I was a student seeing practice thirty odd years ago. I wonder if the Arab shepherds have a name for it – in Lancashire they call it 'sturdy'. The Laristan lamb has got a tapeworm cyst on the brain.

I send Philip for instruments and other equipment while I begin clipping the hair over the soft area of skull. With such a full stomach and no time to waste starving the animal for twenty-four hours or so, I must be wary of the Laristan sheep regurgitating under anaesthetic and then inhaling the stomach contents to produce a lethal pneumonia. To minimise the risk I decide to use the drug xylazine rather than Immobilon and five minutes after Philip returns the ram is flat out and ready for surgery. Scottish shepherds sometimes tackle cases like this themselves by drilling a hole in the skull and sucking out the liquid contents with a straw, a risky business both for sheep and man, for the liquid contains the living laval stage of a tapeworm that will happily establish itself inside human beings. After opening the skin through a small incision I take a narrow trephine and, rather like coring an apple, use it to make a small hole in the skull. Removing the plug of bone I see the silvery white membrane of the meninges that cover the brain bulging up under pressure into the hole. The cyst lies directly underneath. Now I take a hypodermic syringe and gently press the needle through the meninges and the cyst wall. Pulling cautiously back on the syringe plunger I draw off 6 cc of watery liquid before the flow stops. Leaving the needle in place I detach the syringe and fill it with a tiny quantity of weak iodine solution. This I inject through the needle back into the deflated cyst to kill the laval parasite. A puff of antibiotic powder into the hole in the skull, a line of nylon stitches in the skin and all is completed. The whole procedure has taken less than ten minutes. With the pressure removed from its brain the ram should be right as ninepence after a few days recuperation in the quarantine.

A quarter to six; an old Bedou has arrived at the gate with a goat he wants to exchange for a couple of ducks. The gatekeepers are arguing with him when I arrive.

'A goat, doctor – I have told him we want no goats,' says Omar, the chief gatekeeper. He is right, the last thing we need are goats. The Bedous' herds of goats cause enough trouble – getting in through the fencing and acting as reservoirs of disease. The walnut-faced Bedou with a henna-dyed beard stands barefooted in a filthy dish-dasha holding a kid and declaiming about something at great length. From time to time he waves a skinny arm and a hand with long black nails towards the north.

'He says he found this goat in the Hajr, doctor.' My ears prick up. Not a domestic goat then. Something the old fellow came across in the west of Oman. Such nomads have brought rare species dead or alive to the zoo on a number of occasions in the past. I walk over and ask to see the kid. It is a spirited little creature perhaps two months old. God knows how the Arab caught it, it doesn't seem to be injured in any way. Its colour is yellow-buff with dark stripes between the shoulder and down the spine. The tail is black and there are whitish patches on its buttocks and the lower halves of the legs are also white. I feel my heart beat faster when I realise what I am looking at. No domestic goat this – instead I am holding a specimen of one of the least known and most fascinating animals of Arabia – a *Capra aegagrus*, the wild goat of Asia. This is the animal which was probably the first mammal to be domesticated over 8,500 years ago in the mountains of Lebanon and Palestine. Incredibly nimble, able to scale almost vertical rock surfaces, they are shy creatures that live today in the mountains of Greece, Asia Minor, the Caucasus, Iran and Afghanistan. The stone-like hairballs often found in the first stomachs of Wild Goats are still regarded as an antidote to poison and a cure for numerous ailments by the Bedou. Rarely seen in zoos, such truly wild ancestors of the domestic goat are well worth two ducks. It's a stroke of luck that he didn't kill it and eat it – for the flesh is said to be much like venison. After I have arranged for the kid to be housed in the quarantine, I return to the clinic and on the way reflect on the fact that goats such as this one were kept at the oldest zoo on record, that of Tiglath-pileser, King of Assyria around 1000 BC. It is written that 'in the days of cold, frost and rains, in the days of the burning Sirius, he caught in the mountains of Ashur and of Khana and in the Armenian Mountains, male and female Wild Goats, male and female deer with kids, collected them into herds and let them produce. He held these herds to be as valuable as small cattle'.

Six fifteen. As the dusk gathers I set out for a final inspection. The animals, relishing the cool air, are now active and busily scoffing their last feed of the day. A handful of blue-green bee-eaters dart from the bushes to snatch early rising moths. Driving round the zoo perimeter I pay attention to the wire fencing, looking for holes. I hope the foxes and the feral dogs won't find a way in tonight – we have lost too many gazelles to them in the past few weeks.

On my first visit to the zoo in 1979, I had found the veterinary clinics stocked with an anachronistic variety of drugs and instruments – lots of things one would never need and few of the things that are essential even for first aid. Gallons of chloroform (imagine soaking a pad and trying to hold that over the nose of a wildebeeste like they do in gangster movies) but no other sedatives or anaesthetic, innumerable bottles of glycerine (for what I do not know), ancient sacks of rock sulphur and most surprising of all, several pairs of Burdizzo bloodless castrators (in a quarter of a century I haven't castrated a single zoo animal. Reproduction not emasculation is the name of the game). There was also an old ultraviolet lamp that was wired to run off a 12-volt car battery. It had probably been obtained with the idea of diagnosing ringworm infection in the coats of animals. Theoretically, shine a u.v. lamp and the ringworm fungus glows a luminescent yellow or green. Of course, you need the animal in a darkened place to do it and although ringworm is rare in the Al Ain stock, I couldn't imagine ever getting most of them into a dark room without going to the length of full anaesthesia and transporting them in from their enclosures. Anyway, if I suspected the existence of this disease, I would simply sedate the patient by some appropriate method and take a pinch of hair or scraping from the suspicious area for culture by Philip in the lab.

However, the lamp gives me the opportunity to do something I have always wanted. I take it and a lantern with me when I leave the zoo and drive out into the desert away from the barren limestone mountain range of Jebel Hafit across the flat stony land dotted with sparse clumps of tussock grass (*Cymbopogon*) towards the distant dunes. Night in the Rub al Khali, the great sandy desert of Arabia, falls fast and early. The sun, a pond of molten red-gold drains away in the direction of Mecca and the dunes that have lain like sleeping, sunbathing women under the white light of the day take on an even more sensuous almost erotic appearance during the brief dusk. The slopes, mounds, curves, hollows and ridges of sand develop a rich array of shades of colour, gold, sepia, ochre, henna and bronze and their attendant shadows darken and conceal. As the Khamsin, the warm wind of the Empty Quarter, chivies the sand, the sleeping women momentarily stir breast, thigh, calf and groin in the shimmering air. The sky is translucent with smoky swathes of red, violet, pale pink and orange that hurriedly deepen and merge inexorably until all is darkness. The desert at night can be terribly cold but tonight the Khamsin still lingers. All manner of living things are beginning to stir under the cloak of darkness. Creatures who, for a variety of reasons, dare not venture out during the day set about their business. The cool air brings condensation as a source of water for small mammals and other invertebrates. Scorpions leave their hidey-holes to go ahunting and in turn are hunted by rodent, fox and centipede. The saw-scaled viper seeks the jerboa and the jerboa seeks the seeds of the desert tamarisk. I stop the car and walk by lantern light along a wadi. I come across a heap of droppings covered by feasting beetles – Ruppel's Fox, the elusive bat-eared reynard of the deep dunes has been by recently. A lizard with a head of startling electric blue darts under a rock. A toad, yes a toad in the desert, interrupts his gobbling of a locust as my light catches him. I climb up the shallow slope of a dune. A camel spider, a larger and fearsome-looking yellow creature with red jaws, scuttles ahead of me. The Bedou call camel spiders the steeds of the scorpion because they believe the latter ride on their backs, just as men do on camels. On top of the dune there is a feeling of disorientation, of floating in a black sea of stars. The moon is a thin saucer of silver, a holy moon the gate-keepers at the zoo will tell me later.

'When the prophet Mohammed, peace be upon Him, ascended to heaven on his horse, Al Borak, the good horse paused to drink at such a moon.'

About ten years ago an interesting discovery was made. It was that all scorpions dead or alive fluoresce under ultra-violet light. It is to try out the experiment that is the reason for my wandering in the desert this evening. I go back to the jeep and wire up the u.v. light by a long lead to its battery. Now, extinguishing the lantern, I stand in the wadi and switch on the lamp. I find myself standing in a hazy sphere of blue light. The sand close by takes on an eerie dark violet tint and as I bring the lamp close to the ground, I see what looks like a spilled treasure chest of fiery jewels scattered around my feet. The wadi floor is littered with gleaming opals. But the jewels move. They are scorpions – hundreds of them with bodies that are liquid blue-green flame in the glow of the ultraviolet radiation. I move the lamp around – they're everywhere, scuttling about their nightly business, fearful of the many creatures that hunt them. In some deserts there can be as many as 12,000 scorpions per acre and although one might suppose these creatures to be well capable of looking after themselves, possessing venom that they can spray as well as inject and good armour plating, they live hazardous lives spending as little time as possible on the surface of the ground and that generally at night. Cannibals among their own kind, they are also preyed upon by an astonishing range of other creatures which have developed tactics for avoiding the lethal scorpion venom. Some, such as baboons and certain birds, nimbly tear off the sting before gobbling the rest of the scorpion like you would a prawn. Tarantula spiders who also fancy scorpion dinners are conveniently immune to the poison. The use of ultraviolet light to examine animal droppings in which parts of undigested scorpion anatomy continue to fluoresce has enabled scientists to identify the variety of scorpion predators. They include insects such as the mantis, toads (I find it amazing that such soft-bodied amphibians can get away with it), lizards, snakes, all manner of birds, particularly owls, foxes, genets, mongooses, bats, shrews, some rodents and monkeys. With all that mob against them, I feel more than a little sympathy for the horde of hurrying gems as they beat it into the night.

I drive back to the town to 'phone Hanne. She briefs me on the mail and Andrew's movements, tells me Windsor Safari Park's baby dolphin is still doing fine at sixteen weeks of age and solves the technical problem of why the shirts I'm washing in Chris's machine seem to be shrinking. More importantly, after I tell her about the brown bear club and its continual blood loss, she suggests I try Epsikapron powder, the stuff that's so useful for ladies with heavy menstrual periods, in its drinking water. (I do and will find that it works!) I dine at the Ain ul Faydah guest house on humus and badly cooked hamour fish. During the meal I am called to the 'phone. A journalist, Sean Usher of the *Daily Mail*, is calling from London for my views on 'class' in animals. Apparently some folk are objecting to the squirrel being used as the mascot symbol of ROSPA, too 'middle class' an image they say – a typical 'silly season' newspaper puff. What, asks Mr Usher, do I consider to be aristocratic animals? I detest 'class' divisions in human affairs but the question is not to be taken too seriously. I reply that while red deer stags, eagles and falcons, tigers and snow leopards have many of the physical attributes that might traditionally have been equated with 'nobility' – martial bearing, macho looks, etc., on the other hand they lack so-called civilised ways of behaviour, the display of 'humanity' and finer feelings which are seen, I believe, in elephants, whales and dolphins and which might be regarded as marks of nature's gentlemen. Certainly the squirrel with his conservative building-society mind seems rather genteel and 'middle class'. Dogs and cats? Usher asks. Dogs – with their anxiety to please and so often showing their bottoms, essentially very bourgeois. Cats – far more classy and stylish, very much their own men – let us say upper middle class intellectuals. Mice – the proletariat of the animal world. Communist fodder. But rats, far more upwardly mobile – opportunist, flexible, versatile. Ingenious and resistant to oppression. Rats that drink alcohol are more radiation resistant than those who don't booze. It's certainly possible that in a post-nuclear war age rats could be the dominant mammals of the planet – the middle class of the future? The fox – an aristocrat fallen on hard times. A country gent who, like his counterpart among the human uppercrust, is now often found trying to scratch a living in the town. The wolf – a sheep in wolf's clothing. A misunderstood sociable middle-class animal with the undeserved reputation of a robber baron. And finally the hamster. A quarrelsome loner – nothing aristocratic about him, the sort of guy who disagrees with everyone else in the Four Ale bar just to be awkward. A working-class animal undoubtedly but probably one who votes for the Bring Back the Birch and Independence for the Isle of Wight candidate at a general election. It is a dotty conversation but the sort of talking point that might be developed into a pleasant after-dinner topic. How would you socially pigeon-hole say the badger, the magpie or the frog? Which animal does each of your friends most closely remind you of, etc.?

And so to bed. By 10 o'clock I am in my room and my retinue of cockroaches, praying mantises and assorted fearsome looking bugs emerge from every nook and cranny to welcome me. Now I can read undisturbed for an hour before putting out the light. The grey gecko, whose world my room is and who will decimate the creepy-crawlies for me while I sleep, sits on the peeling plaster above my head and watches while I read him a verse or two from the dog-eared book of poetry I carry in The Bag. He seems particularly partial to Omar Khayyam as a prelude to the night's forays.

They say the Lion and the Lizard keep,
The Courts where Jamshyd gloried and drank deep,
And Bahram, that great Hunter – the wild Ass
Stamps ore his Head but cannot break his sleep.

Later the fabled animals of Asia continued to run and soar through my dreams. It's refreshing to be back in general practice in Arabia felix.

3 Bright Bears

A column of minute black ants are filing into the bottom of my left trouser leg as I squat in the sand by a grizzled stump of dead acacia bush. I must not move, ants or no ants. I am hot and smelly, clad in a threadbare tunic dark with sweat stains borrowed straight from the back of a Baluch an hour before. Across my lap the rifle lies cocked, its shiny barrel camouflaged with tied-on wisps of alfalfa. The wind in my face is as the blast from a bread oven door; it bears the faint odours of goat and baked rock. This is not a visit to the Afghan mujahideen in the Khyber Pass. I am waiting for an Eland bull that stands 300 metres away, wary ears pricked, nostrils dilated, head held high. Will he come within the range of my weapon, so that I can dart him for movement to another section of the zoo where a newly arrived female awaits? He knows his regular Baluchi keeper well but I, for all the dissembling, must still smell, look and move completely wrong. That is why I crouch motionless – hoping the bull will think I'm his friend at prayer or relieving himself – something he sees several times every day. What am I doing here, I think? Why do we spend our lives *caring* in the widest sense of the word for animals? I'd long argued as an after-dinner debating topic that logically there is no reason why in a Judaeo-Christian culture we should accord any status, let alone 'rights', to lower animals. Does not man have dominion over other creatures from both an evolutionary and theological point of view? For Christians the only creature with a 'soul', made in the image of God, is man. Christ's gospel was to man not blue whales, pandas or pekinese. Of course, there are difficulties posed by evolution theory and the possible development over millions of years of soul in the manner of a physical organ, and the writings of Teilhard de Chardin continue to exercise my mind. But what, as a Christian, is the theology of animals – if any?

The matter came up again in the unlikely setting of a Marguerita cocktail party last night. Again we discussed the perennial problems. Why is cruelty to animals wrong? Some theologians argue that it is bad because of its brutalising effect *on the human* – in other words, if one could inflict cruelty (and perhaps we do when we use fly sprays, modern agricultural methods, etc.) *without* brutalising ourselves, then it's OK. After all it's only the human soul that the theologian is concerned with. But somehow there is a *feeling* of the intrinsic wrongness of cruelty. Then a lady sitting next to me said something which seemed to illuminate the whole conundrum. God she said is love. That's the key the core the sum of Christian theology. It's love – of creatures, of the world, of everything that matters, that must motivate. The logic of caring for animals is, she stated, that we as Christians must *love* with the same all encompassing reverence the totality of created things – stones, seashells, slugs, clay and rain as well as dolphins and bushbabies. The words of St Paul and the Islamic, Buddhist and Hindu attitudes to the holiness of all things are at one. So, this morning waiting for the Eland to make his mind up I feel that I developed my spirit a bit last night thanks to the good lady and the Margueritas. My ruminations aren't producing anything much in the way of Taylor–Eland good vibrations just now, however, for the bull suddenly decides I'm trouble, spins on his hind hooves and gallops away. The ants are almost at my groin. I'll try again tomorrow morning.

There are less high-faluting reasons why I enjoy being among animals – they make such good friends and acquaintances. And I don't just mean the animals of so-called higher intelligence. Intelligence measurement has proved to be a contentious and complex enough subject within *one* species, Homo sapiens, without venturing farther afield into casting judgement on creatures with which one cannot even communicate. If different cultural backgrounds between races and nationalities have bedevilled comparative human intelligence studies, how much more inexact must be the classification of the so-called lower creatures. Here again environment, upbringing, 'culture' must be powerful factors – Einstein wouldn't be rated very highly in the world of, say, the great white shark and Oxford dons would have a hard time keeping up with frog-eating bats in *their* world. Every living creature fills its biological niche because it is a victor, a top-of-the-form prize-winner in the evolutionary race, the survival of the fittest. Intelligence is a philosophical concept, not an exact science and means one thing when applied to a toad in a greenhouse and something totally different and unrelated to a man in a council house in Peckham Rye. But just as bright, well-educated, 'intelligent' folk don't necessarily make the best friends or companions and where simpler individuals can display the greatest qualities of loyalty, devotion, humour and quick-thinking – so too with animals. I've written elsewhere about the chimpanzees who delight in making asses out of people, of orangs with post-natal depression, of lions that are crafty in picking individuals to urinate upon, of mischievous and bawdy parrots and kindly dolphins. I've seen turtles as faithful to their master as sheepdogs and a mature male gorilla who adores being dressed up and having his photograph taken. Give this latter individual a hat, a gown, socks and gloves and in no time at all he's posing fully garbed like an Edwardian dandy with as vain and pompous an expression on his face as you're ever likely to see – and like the aristocrat he is, he prefers having a dresser in attendance to make sure the buttons are correctly done, the fitting neat and even at the shoulders and the headgear at a rakish angle.

Now perhaps you might not think that bears are very

bright beasts – more lumbering, grumbling, furry dustbins who are either sleeping or on the look out for grub. Not so. I find bears fascinating if rather untidy men of the world. Yes, they do have a weakness for food bordering on gluttony. As a consequence they often get upset stomachs – generally quickly cured by a day without food or water and keeping them on a strict diet of ice cubes or, much preferred, ice lollies. Bears are dangerous animals and in recent years there has been an increasing number of problems in the North American national parks where man and bear come to cross purposes over territorial rights and food supply. Both polar and brown bears in the United States have taken to raiding human habitations whether they be town houses, log cabins or campers' tents for the easy pickings among food waste or sometimes where people have foolishly put out food by design for Ole Bruin. It's had a corrupting effect on the bears and although some humans have been killed or injured by the powerful animals, it's the bears that have tended to suffer most. One curious and tragic occurrence has happened as a result of darting 'rogue' or persistently trash-can-foraging bears with anaesthetic and then transporting them to more isolated and man-free stretches of forest many miles away by helicopter. This well-intentioned forced exile hasn't worked for long with many individuals. They simply find their way back to where they know the goodies are. The anaesthetic generally used for this translocation procedure has been phencyclidine, the drug sometimes used by junkies and known by them as 'angel dust'. In humans it can produce bizarre hallucinations even more potent than those resulting from LSD and, very significantly, can cause permanent psychological disturbances even after a single dose. I was one of the first veterinary surgeons to use phencyclidine in zoo animals and helped in its development in Great Britain in the late fifties. For its time it was a major breakthrough for those of us needing a powerful low-volume stable drug which would work via any route – by mouth, injected under the skin anywhere on the body or intramuscularly. It was perfect for the then newly developed flying dart. I rarely use it nowadays and legal production in Great Britain ceased a number of years ago. But it is still available in the USA and some other countries and as I say it has been the backbone of the bear translocation scheme. Some bears then, persistently returning like bad pennies, have been darted several times and the effect on their brains of the multiple doses of phencyclidine seems in some cases to have turned them, as in the case of some human beings, into dangerous psychotics. The ursine prodigal sons have come home not simply with a lip-smacking grunt of delight at the prospect of joining some unsuspecting camper's barbecue or disgorging a favourite dustbin of its half-eaten sandwiches but with occasionally deranged and unpredictably aggressive mentalities.

A similar case occurred when I was called to Belle Vue in 1963 to look at a young Himalayan bear which had become quickly blind with cataracts after being hand reared when its mother rejected it. In those days I saw a large number of bottle-reared exotic animals with similar loss of sight, caused by the normally transparent lenses of the eyes becoming at first bluish then milky and finally white and completely impervious to light. They included camels, wallabies, lions, tigers and leopards. A few were true diabetics but all I am sure were in some way linked to the quantity or type of sugar that we used in artificial feeding at that time. Matt Kelly, the Head Keeper, was deeply attached to the Himalayan bear. He it was who had nursed it, bottle-fed it every two hours at first, slept with it by his bedside, coped with infant diarrhoea and played with it for long hours on the lawns outside the elephant house to the delight of Matt, the bear and thousands of visitors.

'Is there *nothing*, ye can do,' Matt had asked when I gave him my diagnosis. 'It bumps into every blessed thing, but it's, well, such a fine boyo – ye can't mean we got to put it . . .

to see it away!' He had the bear, now as big as an Alsatian dog, squatting patiently at his heels and licking his boots as he spoke.

'It's irreversible, Matt,' I replied. 'Could you imagine what a life it would lead – blind in the bear enclosure. Suppose it falls into the moat!' The Irishman gritted his teeth like he always did at times of stress and looked me straight in the eyes.

'Would they put you down if it happened to you, son?'

'No, of course not.'

'So – you're the one who was telling me about the dog cataracts ye'd been having a go at at Rochdale. And last April ye spent some time at the Eye Infirmary with whats-is-name, that big eye fellow, Stuart Scott. What was all that for then, eh? Chatting up the nurses? Playing at doctors?' Matt was steaming straight for one of his rare but awesome bouts of choler. The storm clouds lifted from his face the instant I agreed to attempt to remove the cataractous lens from one eye. The operation three days later went well – the technique and approach was the same as in a dog or a human being, or as I was to use on the young zebra Tatu in Kenya some years later. Under phencyclidine anaesthesia I opened the tough cornea just in front of its junction with the white sclera, dissolved the attachment of the lens with some enzyme, took hold of the lens by means of a tiny suction device, teased it out of the eyeball and stitched up the incision with black silk after leaving a bubble of air inside the eye to stop the iris sticking to the back of the cornea before a new supply of aqueous humour, the 'water' in the eye, had filtered in. Matt was delighted but I warned him that we weren't home and dry yet.

'There can be all sorts of post-operative complications – haemorrhage into the eye, adhesions, opportunist infections. You can't keep a bear in a dim lit ward resting with an eye patch on. And I'll have to knock it out two or three more times to check on progress and finally remove the stitches.'

Matt had a great relationship with the animal but couldn't hold its head still enough for me to do anything close to the eye. As I had predicted the bear was given phencyclidine on two more occasions. The eye healed well, the pupil reflex became strong, the retina looked perfect and best of all the Head Keeper reported that although it had obviously got a blind side, the bear rarely bumped into things any more. But although we didn't notice it at first the animal's temperament had changed. It became capricious and moody. It would suddenly snap aggressively at Matt's hand as he bent to stroke it and work itself into a fury when he tried to gentle it.

Little or nothing was known about the psychological after-effects of phencyclidine in the early sixties. True there were reports of satyrism (prolonged sexual excitement) in some of the early experiments on humans. Nobody had reported anything suggesting mental disturbance in animals, however. Eventually the Himalayan bear became so delinquent and uncontrollable that Matt had to remove it permanently into the bear enclosure. There it continued to behave erratically, quarrelling with or shunning its own kind and we had to resign ourselves sadly to the fact that the once cuddly bear was now an antisocial misfit. Even daily doses of tranquillisers in its food didn't alleviate matters. In the end Matt moved it to a place where it could be kept alone and, much as we detested solitary animals, it seemed somewhat happier there, although plainly afflicted from time to time with black and mysterious moods.

I haven't had another bear like that and looking back, particularly in the light of the recent problems in the American parks, I feel fairly certain that unwittingly we too had altered, or perhaps it would be more accurate to say bent, the mind of an animal with the 'angel dust'. Like the Sorcerer's Apprentice one doesn't always know what one might be releasing when giving new drugs to wild animals, and the case of the Himalayan bear grieves me deeply now that I know what probably happened.

The young polar bears at Chessington Zoo possess minds as sharp as needles. They have as we say in Lancashire, 'all their chairs at home' and no mistake. They were a boisterous pair of cubs when I first went to select them at Karlsruhe Zoo in Germany. Now three years later in the new polar bear exhibit at Chessington, they entertain the visitors with their joyful water games and keep their keepers firmly under control. Take the male, for example. Being an independent minded sort of chap with a fine creamy coat he rather enjoys napping outdoors. True he's been provided with a luxurious snug den indoors but with the summer having been so long and glorious this year, he fancied the stars over Kingston-upon-Thames for his blanket, and the moon which looks just the same from Surrey, Karlsruhe or the Arctic pack-ice to a drowsy bear or anybody else for that matter, for his nightlight. So why not snuggle down on the cool rocks by the blue water – what's wrong with that? Ginger, the Head Keeper, had different views. Not that Ginger doesn't appreciate the wonders of the firmament and such alfresco pleasures, nor is he what my grandmother called a 'worrit', concerned lest the night air in Chessington might bring on coughs and sneezes unheard of in Greenland bears. No, Ginger liked to have his bears safely locked in at night – secure from vandals, those common pests of zoological gardens who might harm the animals or in some way enable them to escape. Polar bears going walkabout on the A3 would give Ginger a migraine considerably greater than that traditionally suffered by bears with sore heads.

The Head Keeper had personally attended the two bears ever since they arrived and they knew him, his voice and his bucket full of meat, bread, vegetables and fish very well. At 7 o'clock Ginger's deep voice would boom, 'Grub up!' and the polar bears would sensibly trot into their dens for supper, whereupon Ginger would release the lever that lowered the door grille behind them. Simple. Until Clyde, the male bear, decided to sleep outside. It isn't any use shouting at a polar bear (even in Eskimo or in Clyde's case perhaps, German). Being well brought up they pretend they haven't heard. It does no good poking a stick at one (not that Ginger would ever think of hurting one of his animals) for it would simply take the stick away from you with its powerful paws and jaws and chomp it up. Squirting it with a hosepipe fills it with deep contentment. Waving a plastic snake in front of it (a trick that works with apes) is plain stupidity – who ever heard of snakes in the Arctic? Making a loud noise – say, by banging two dustbin lids together or bringing along a transistor with 'Status Quo' on at full volume – is to make a futile exhibition of oneself in front of the visitors. Such a cacophony cannot compare to the *Titanic* cracking up on the Greenland sea ice or the thunder of the waves off Novaya Zemlya. Ginger had one ploy at his command only: to place the food in the den and be quick at letting the door down. Well, well – Clyde saw that one coming and countered by lying flat out across the threshold half in and half out of the den and with a great stretch of a forepaw hooking the food out. One–love to Clyde! Ginger's next refinement of his ploy was to place the food in a compact pile as far away from the door as possible and well beyond stretched-out-on-a-rack-polar-bear distance. Clyde considered this the first evening Ginger tried it and experimented with a quick dash in towards the food, but as soon as he was aware of the door coming down he was even quicker at turning tail and beating it just in time. It wasn't quite one–all. Ginger hadn't nabbed Clyde but on the other hand Clyde hadn't nabbed any supper. So stalemate is perhaps a better term. Next day, Clyde looked hungrily at the heap of food deep in the den but having worked out in his mind the mathematics of it, the time, the distance, the effect of gravity on the gate, the predicted reflex time of Ginger's arm, he realised that supper was, by all the laws of Newtonian physics, out of reach good and proper. But he was getting hungrier. Ginger, proud of the layers of fat beneath Clyde's skin and his glossy coat, was well aware that the bear could easily afford several days without food if it came to that. Clyde, on the other hand, was happy being plump, was not into Jane Fonda work-outs or losing weight by crash diets. He liked his victuals and the odd sweet and peanut, naughtily thrown over the barrier by visitors who ignored the 'no feeding' notice during the day, but whilst appreciated they were no substitute for this ursine trencherman. Ginger decided to wait. Surely eventually the polar bear stomach juices would drive it into the den for those delectable herrings and chunks of beef. Then WHAMMO!

Clyde, meanwhile, elected for a bit of lateral thinking, a touch of the Edward De Bono's. He approached the problem rather like boy scouts and officer cadets who have to tackle initiative tests, such as how do you get across a river using only a box of drawing pins and a pair of pyjamas. He looked around his enclosure with its rocks and pool. No drawing pins or pyjamas – only a large blue plastic barrel bobbing in the water, the one that the two bears played water polo with during the day. Eureka! (Have you solved the puzzle yet, intelligent reader?) That evening along came Ginger yet again with fresh food to put in the distant corner of the den. As usual the Head Keeper then moved to the lever controlling the door and waited expectantly. Surely tonight Clyde would be sleeping indoors with a full tum. Impassively (he didn't want to give the game away too quickly by smirking), Clyde turned his back on the den and with masterly aplomb belly-flopped into the water. He paddled lazily over to the blue barrel, grasped it between his paws and threw it on to the rocks. Then he hauled himself out, ambled nonchalantly over to the barrel and rolled it towards the den. Once there he carefully placed the barrel firmly under the door grille, wedging it impudently and most decidedly open. Satisfied with his stratagem, the bear then sauntered into the den gave Ginger a look, well you know how inscrutable, how Chinese, polar bears are, and settled down to dine. Game set and match. Clyde slept outdoors the rest of the summer but naturally, being nobody's fool, when the weather broke he removed his barrel and took up residence again.

4 *Another Elephant, Another Place*

It is an understatement to say that I experienced a sense of profound *déjà vu* in helping to recreate the tragic story of Mary the elephant when the BBC began filming the first series of 'One By One', the drama based on my first three volumes of autobiography. As technical advisers, Andrew and I enjoyed working with the Special Effects and Make-Up Departments in attempting to make the scenes where 'veterinary' work was carried out look as realistic as possible. For the story of Jane, the post-natal depressive orang which my wife had nursed back to health and happiness, we supervised the modelling by the BBC Special Effects Department of an uncannily accurate 'stillborn' foetus complete with red hair in all the right places and an umbilical cord. It wasn't possible, however, for us to find an orang-outang female in any zoo in Great Britain that was tame and reliable enough to nurse the dead infant and then let Heather James, the actress, gently take it from her. So we arranged through Marty Dinnes, our associate in California, to use the incredibly talented male orang (but which actually has the facial features of a female) that was involved in the Clint Eastwood 'Every Which Way But Loose' movie. This incredible ape flew in to England with two human 'minders', acted the part perfectly with never a fluffed line or missed cue, the whole filming being done in conditions of strict quarantine supervised on behalf of the Ministry of Agriculture by myself, and then after a couple of days hopped back on the plane for Los Angeles several thousand dollars the richer. For scenes which required an injured tiger, a real live Bengal male from Chipperfields Circus that needed its ingrowing toe-nails cutting was used together with a stuffed model of a tiger bought from a museum. The BBC technicians built three ingenious motorised pumps into the latter, one to simulate thoracic (chest) breathing, the second for abdominal breathing (seen mainly when an animal is relaxed or under sedation) and the third to produce a brilliantly natural pulse in the jugular vein of the 'doped' tiger. All the mechanical devices were controlled by wires that exited from the corpse via the beast's anus and ran out of camera shot to an engineer.

It was great fun helping Joyce Dean, the head of the make-up team and an expert at constructing counterfeit wounds, tumours and every sort of pathological lesion. Joyce and her lady assistants worked off photographs of real-live injuries and disease and from medical textbooks. I was astonished how with plastic, waxes, paints, gums and a host of professional tricks they could make abscesses, gangrene, lacerations, fistulas and cancers that I would have diagnosed as genuine at point blank range. When a 'tumour' had to be surgically removed from the leg of an elephant, the plastic growth, with a spongy base soaked in theatrical blood and 'innards' of strips of fillet steak which I had sutured into place, was glued to the unconcerned animal's thigh with false moustache adhesive. It was covered with a perfectly matching patch of grey plastic which had been made from a cast of the area and bore all its natural elephantine wrinkles and fissures. We had three such model tumours. One for long shots, another for close-up work when my hands would be seen making the actual incision and a third just in case of emergencies. There were also other models for various stages of the operation – with the tumour half out, fully out, half sutured and fully sutured. Joyce and I lovingly used obstetric jelly (to make tissue glisten), meat, sprays of water and various kinds of artificial gore to dress these expensive preparations just before the cameras rolled. For the spurting arteries, either a fine tube leading to a syringe that was out of shot was used, or, as on one memorable occasion, I lay on the floor beneath the camera and at the appropriate moments squirted Rob Heyland playing Don Turner (me) with blood supposedly from an artery he had just severed. It wasn't as easy as it sounds. Take after take I kept squirting too hard or too gently, too far to the left or too far to the right – the director didn't want Rob to be soaked in scarlet like some Hammer film victim (the programme was for family viewing at 7.15 on a Sunday night), and every time I got it wrong Maggie the wardrobe mistress had to find Rob another clean identical operating gown.

'Blood' on a grand scale was needed when we filmed the story about Cuddles the Flamingo Park killer whale who haemorrhaged severely from intestinal ulcerations turning her 300,000-gallon pool a horrific red. The incident was to be re-enacted at Marineland Côte d'Azur in France and I was given the task of deciding how to do it effectively and safely. The French pool is far bigger even than Flamingo Park's and contains three big whales. I had to come up with some substance that would colour a large volume of sea water crimson but not stain the pool walls or the whales' white patches of skin and would not irritate their eyes in the slightest or have any harmful effects if swallowed. Blood from the slaughter house, stage 'blood', and deep red dyes of certain kinds were all unsuitable on grounds of hygiene, cost or insolubility in sea water. Also, after filming the effect, the red water had to be got rid of. Marineland waste water runs via a short sluggish stream directly into the sea – 300,000 gallons of red liquid would have the Côte d'Azur municipalities, with pollution troubles enough as it is without a Taylor-made 'red tide', hopping mad. Once during the previous year, when a sea elephant at Marineland had had an acute vaginal haemorrhage after a rather vigorous mating, the blood had been enough to redden the water distinctly where the stream entered the ocean – and the volume of blood lost on that occasion could only have been perhaps 10 or 12 pints. So we needed a red colouring agent that could be destroyed after use – preferably by liquid chlorine which every marineland has in abundance to purify its water. The answer seemed to be food colouring and to this end I investigated the sort of liquids used for making cake icings or jelly a nice and non-toxic shade of red. A little bottle of the stuff was purchased from a grocer, mixed with a bucket of sea water and hey presto – bloody water! Best of all, when a drop or two of liquid chlorine bleach was added, the colour vanished. I arranged for the BBC to obtain the pure chemical in concentrated form and in due course the props lady arrived in France with a 2-kilo tin of amaranth in powder form – twice as much as we calculated would be necessary to turn the whole pool scarlet.

A few hours before the shooting of the Cuddles scene, Mike Riddell the Marineland Director banged on my hotel room door. He was in a state of considerable consternation. John Kershaw the Head Trainer had just decided to try out a teaspoonful of the red dye on a sink full of sea water in the fish kitchen. Voila! the sink, much of the kitchen and John himself were a deep red and going deeper! The chemical's action seemed to be intensifying by the minute and the place looked like a vision of hell with John as Old Nick himself. Worse, the red was staining skin, tiles – anything in fact – and wasn't being neutralised by liquid chlorine. John's pillar-box red hands and face (he'd thoughtfully stuck his head in the dyed water and opened his eyes just to prove for sure that there would be no irritation to mammalian eyes) were dramatic to behold.

'Put that in the pool and I'll have black and red killer whales, David,' said Michael himself rather pink in the face. 'And with the chlorine not knocking the stuff out, the stream and the sea outside Marineland are going to be in a hell of a mess. If the villa owners next door open their curtains tomorrow morning on to a view of something like this they will (a) die of shock or (b) have the environmental health people here in minutes. Apart from the police who'll think they've got a mega-murders on the Rue Morgue on their hands. The filming is off!' I was discomfited to say the least. The food colouring had worked well in England. The powder concentrate was the same stuff for sure. Could there be some difference in the sea water qualities between Southampton and Nice? – it seemed unlikely. The possibility of having brought a forty-man BBC crew out to Nice on a fool's errand was firmly on the cards.

I dashed round to the Marineland with Michael to see for myself the results of John's dabbling in kitchen sink chemistry. It was true – the Head Keeper looked as if he'd just been flayed alive on an Aztec sun altar.

'I only used a teaspoon of the bloody, literally, stuff,' said John forlornly, 'now what am I going to do?' I decided to re-run his experiment. Filling the sink again I took the smallest quantity of the dye from the tin – about as much as would cover a match head – and dropped it into the water. The fine powder dissolved and in no time at all I had a sink full of blood. I swirled my hands in the stuff and took them out – they weren't stained. John had unwittingly used far, far more than was necessary. This amaranth was incredibly potent. Somewhere our calculations had gone awry and the BBC had bought enough dye to keep all the bakers and confectioners in France supplied with colouring for a century. My heart in my mouth, I poured a little chlorine liquid into the sink. The red water was instantly bleached. Greatly relieved and educated in the efficiency of modern dyes, I got to work sponging John down with a strong chlorine solution quickly neutralised, before he could be burnt, by a rinse of hypo. He returned by and by to his normal healthy tan. The Cuddles shoot at Marineland went ahead. Gory water swirled round Kim the killer whale playing the part of Cuddles and we used in total only half a coffee cup of the red dye. When the red water was eventually drained away to the sea, it was eliminated by the chlorine pumps in Marineland's massive water treatment plant and not a drop of the fake haemoglobin escaped to sully the waters of the Mediterranean off the Boulevard des Anglais. By a peculiar coincidence the fountain in the main square of Antibes spouted claret-coloured water one miraculous morning a few days later. Rob Heyland, straightfaced, 'arrived' on the scene and sat on the fountain's edge offering tastings of a bottle of real wine which he claimed just to have filled from the apparently transmuted water. Rob melted away into the crowd when a posse of flustered municipal officials and a policeman hove into view, but not before his *degustation* had made a small percentage of the more superstitious citizenry speculate openly on whether, it being the ninth of October, the feast day of St Denis, patron saint of France, they had not witnessed a most wondrous sign from heaven.

The BBC team did acknowledge me as the unrivalled expert in one rather narrow field of special effects – the making of vomit and diarrhoea. My masterpiece, a 100-gallon tank of elephant diarrhoea so perfect that Elephant Bill wouldn't have spotted the difference, was hand mixed by me (volunteers were thin on the ground that day) from milk, bison droppings, white and yellow paint. They talk of it still in the corridors of the BBC. While on matters scatological, I learned from a friend today that archaeologists have a word for faecal matter that they find in their digs – coprolite. What a wonderfully useful word with such a polite and scientific ring to it. It sounds like the name of a rare mineral or a pretty seashell. I can understand how vitally important it is for scholars to possess such a word. Imagine a learned thesis that could do no better than . . . 'and in the ante-room of King Nebuchadnezzar's Palace we came upon a 3·46-

kilogram mound of turds'. No, that is inconceivable. Should the demand for my services in creating theatrical droppings ever reach the pitch where I have to give up the veterinary profession, I shall have it emblazoned on my visiting cards – 'David C. Taylor. Stage and Screen Coprolitist. No job too big.'

Of course, in all the filming not one animal was ever hurt or upset in the slightest. Skilful editing of the film mixed shots of fake and live animals and many of the close-up operations were actually done on plastic skin stretched across a bale of straw. Nevertheless, we did get letters from viewers complaining bitterly about the animals we must have hurt or even killed to make the films. It was nonsense – these good folk had been deceived by the modern film-makers art, though I do think they should have had the wit to suspect as much before dashing to put pen to paper. But the excellent scene which brought back so many poignant memories to me because of its closeness to the actual happening twenty-five years before was the one where Mary the elephant had to have a tooth removed. Watching Peter Jeffries, Jimmy Ellis and Rob Heyland act out at Dudley Zoo what had been an almost unbearably searing few hours at Belle Vue when I as a young zoo vet had tackled my first bit of elephant dentistry, was truly moving. The way we did it was to anaesthetise lightly one of Chipperfield's elephants that needed a blood sampling and chiropody as a matter of course, but to do the gargantuan operation of removing the great tooth with chisels, mallets and crow-bars on a fantastic model of an elephant's head. This wonder took months to construct by Special Effects and cost many thousands of pounds but when finished it did everything a live elephant's head does, except think. It rolled its eyes, blinked, waggled its ears, drooled saliva, moved its tongue and even emitted a vapoury breath (there was a man crouched inside the model with a steaming electric kettle!). The model was anatomically perfect from the texture of its skin to the in-depth structure of the jaw bone. But there was one bit that wasn't fake, that was the tooth which would be removed during the operation. It was the actual tooth removed from Mary all those years before and kept by me as a souvenir. We made a 'root abscess' out of a blob of sponge and tied it on to one of the roots with nylon thread. The tooth was set into the fibreglass jaw and surrounded by pink latex gums. In order to let Rob do some realistic chipping with his dental instruments, a weakened area of fibreglass had been prepared and filled with a special plaster. Further, his chisels were made of aluminium so that he could hit as hard as he liked and yet make little headway – it was important to simulate the arm-numbing effort that took six hours in the original. The tooth socket was fitted with a blood tube which would disgorge just the right amount of gore as the extraction progressed. Final touches such as capillary ooze and mucus were added at the last moment by Joyce and me using crimson blusher and K-Y jelly. All in all the filming of the Mary tooth incident was a great success and the reliving of it left me emotionally as well as physically exhausted when the Director, Chris Baker, called 'wrap' at the end of the day.

Letters really rolled in after the episode was screened. 'Disgusting, taking a tooth out of an elephant just to make a film.' 'Immoral to first butcher and then kill the poor creature.' (The 'dead' unbreathing elephant sequence was achieved by freezing the frame of the reclining but very much alive Chipperfield animal.) Some letters positively frothed with obscenities. One lady even wrote to say that 'It was quite inaccurate – her husband had worked in a zoo and new about such things – that tooth was far too small and anyway elephants' teeth didn't look like that all.' Well, I wonder what old Mary would have thought about that – it was her tooth, weighing 4 kilos, that had caused the bouts of awful toothache which led to the real-life operation, her death from hypostatic pneumonia and indirectly the television series. I can imagine her rolling up her dear old dusty trunk and blinking those dark and limpid eyes and even interrupting the munching of one of her favourite custard pies if anyone had suggested she wasn't a real elephant with very real teeth.

While filming the first series a curious coincidence occurred which in many ways brings the Mary saga and its recreation on film full circle. Mary Chipperfield 'phoned to say that some friends of hers had an elephant act in a small Italian circus at the time touring in Spain. The circus was indeed small, for the troupe of elephants consisted of one Asiatic elephant which was the light of Mary's friends' lives. They doted on it and literally lived with it – they had one half of the elephant wagon, the elephant had the other. It was their livelihood, their child, their best friend. And now it was very sick in the port of Alcudia, Majorca. Could I go and see it? What Mary described over the telephone sounded very much like tooth trouble. The middle-aged female elephant hadn't eaten or drunk a drop for three days. It couldn't sleep and was obviously in great pain somewhere in the mouth. Normally as handleable as a pussy cat, it wouldn't let its owners go anywhere near the jaw and was uncharacteristically and constantly in a foul temper. It sounded exactly like another Mary in urgent need of dentistry. Once again I booked a seat on the last flight to Majorca (the island seemed to be becoming zoological centre of Europe in those days) and packed The Bag with a selection of more unusual surgical instruments – The Burglar's Kit. Several stainless steel masonry chisels, 12-inch and 18-inch long jemmies and my 'bodger' – a heavy iron-headed mallet. In addition I decided upon a horsegag – a strong F-shaped device that could be useful in keeping the narrow jaws of an anaesthetised elephant open. The Bag, of course, contained as part of its permanently resident collection of paraphernalia, specialised anaesthetics, emergency drugs, a variety of syringes and needles and the basic array of surgical instruments – sufficient to do say a Caesarean on a large animal or explore inside a stomach or two. Going through the security check at Heathrow, The Bag was taken to one side after passing through the X-ray machine. A security man opened it and carefully scrutinised the contents. The motley collection of chisels and jemmies and the pack containing scalpels sharper than razors he ignored completely. What did fascinate him, however, was the horsegag which he grim-facedly withdrew and stared at as he turned it in his hands.

'I'm afraid you can't carry that sir.'

'Why not?'

'Because . . . because I'm afraid you can't.'

The gag is a fairly simple device, the F-shape being composed of one vertical and two horizontal bars of chrome steel set in a simple wooden handle. The two horizontal bars move towards or away from one another by means of a screw and wing-nut at the bottom of the vertical bar. There are no sharp edges or dangerous points for obvious reasons. It's actually a bit of an antique but it functions well enough.

'But it's not a weapon, couldn't be used as one,' I protested. Imagine bursting into the cockpit brandishing the thing and saying to the pilot, 'Say "ah" while I put this in to keep your gob open – or fly me to Moscow instanter!'

'I don't know what it is but it . . . it looks suspicious.'

I suppose held on its side it does bear a very faint resemblance to the basic shape of a Sten gun but it is all quite obviously solid. There is no trigger or magazine and nothing barrel-like. Taking the gag from him I remove the wing-nut and separated the two pieces of stout metal. They looked far more innocent than the gleaming chisels.

'There – you see – it's as simple as that.'

The security man picked up the bits and shook his head.

'No way you can carry it on that 'plane sir!'

'Ridiculous,' I retorted. 'It's a gag, a thing for holding an elephant's mouth open . . .'

'Yes sir – and I'm Little Red Riding Hood.'

'And I'm only carrying hand baggage on an urgent visit.

I don't want to lose it or time by having it go as checked baggage.'

The security man inhaled a deep and officious chestful of air and stared at the ceiling as he uttered his final comments. 'It goes in the hold, sir, or it don't go at all.'

The poor old gag was eventually carried away between finger and thumb at arm's length by another security man, who regarded it with an expression more appropriate to something like a cross between an overripe kipper and a primed hand grenade. It travelled as checked baggage and mercifully arrived safely in Majorca.

By the time I had driven across the island to the northern port of Alcudia where the sick elephant was, it was late in the evening, dark and moonless. Signor and Signora Crona turned out to be a middle-aged couple who had been all their lives in the circus. Both small in stature, they seemed an industrious and friendly pair with none of the theatrical flashiness one often finds in the continental circus troupers. It was difficult to imagine them in greasepaint and spangles out in the sawdusted ring. Both of them greeted me effusively and although they politely offered me coffee after the journey, I declined and asked them to take me at once to see the elephant and tell me the history on the way. They were obviously deeply troubled and my concern to cut unnecessary pleasantries appeared to cheer them up enormously.

'Don't worry,' I said, as we walked round to the elephant's half of their long trailer. 'We'll soon sort it out.' Not a very prudent thing to say before even having had a glimpse of one's patient. Sr Crona gave a little yelp of joy, grabbed my hand and kissed it warmly.

The circus had moved on by ferry to Minorca. The Cronas and their elephant were all that was left behind. On the telephone I had insisted that they didn't move the animal, mainly because Majorca is logistically far more convenient that Minorca for me and I have Marineland and other contacts there to back me up if necessary. The elephant truck stood on a small patch of ground just off the quayside. There were no lights either outside or inside the vehicle. I would have to conduct my initial examination of the elephant with the aid of a torch. Sr Crona unlocked and swung back the double doors and handed me the flashlight. I played the beam up and down an enormous but rather thin-looking Indian elephant which stood facing me. Its face, full of character, was drawn and tense. The eyes were tired with drooping lids and congested whites. Thin ropes of saliva hung down from the half-open mouth as it fidgeted irritably and looked at me with none of the tolerant curiosity that I associate with newly introduced elephant acquaintances.

'Brave, brave, brave!' I whispered gently the words of circus German that are used internationally among elephant men to soothe and encourage, and fractionally moved the hand not holding the torch towards her head. It hadn't travelled 2 inches before she lashed out angrily with her trunk and emitted a piercing squeal of anger and anguish. I wasn't quite fast enough in jumping back. The trunk tip whipped the side of my head and it felt like I'd been punched by a rubber cosh. This unhappy animal was clearly enduring intense pain.

'OK, close her up,' I said rubbing my singing head. 'Tooth trouble of some sort without a doubt. I'll have to knock her down first thing in the morning.' In this place with no lights, no indoor quarters, no circus tent, it would have been impossible to operate at night. Signora Crona was on the verge of tears when we sat down in a nearby bar to discuss my plans.

'But doctor – do you think she has a chance? Will she be safe with an anaesthetic? Where will you do it? She's our life – she's all we got.'

The television blared at full volume as it does in all Spanish bars, a group of locals were laughing over a dice game they were playing in a corner and the patron and his wife and daughters were stacking chairs on tables for it was near closing time. Thank God it's out of season and tourists are few I thought. Mary the Belle Vue elephant is always there when I have to deal with tooth problems in others of her species. But a quarter of a century on I don't feel sick in the pit of my stomach any more when I know I've got to anaesthetise the largest of all terrestrial mammals, a pachyderm that can weigh in at over 6,000 kilos. Mary died because good as they were, the zoo anaesthetics of her day were not good enough. They were neither short acting nor reversible. Now I regard the elephant as one of the easiest and most predictable of all exotic species to put under – providing you follow certain simple guidelines. Strange as it may seem the dose of the preferred anaesthetic needed to anaesthetise a big African bull elephant is less than that for an average deer. As I sipped my coffee and nightcap of Hierbas, I outlined to the Cronas my plans for the morning.

'We will begin at 7 o'clock – before any tourists emerge. I will put her down on the promenade itself – it's smooth, clean and there's plenty of space there. All I want you to do is to lay a deep 4-metre square of straw and provide me with two buckets of water, soap and a towel.'

'That is all?'

'Yes – and now I'm going to bed. I'm tired but I will be on the promenade exactly at seven.'

'But it's close to the beach – how will I chain her up out there? What if she won't get up?'

Sr Crona looked wretchedly gloomy and his wife dabbed her eyes with a handkerchief.

'All you have to do Signor is to bring her out of the truck, take her to the middle of the straw patch and get her to stand still for a couple of seconds while I give her a jab – with any luck she'll be back in the truck, all finished by nine.'

'She won't have eaten or drunk anything for four and a half days by then – can she take it doctor?'

The lack of fluid intake did concern me somewhat but I've had elephants go for much longer than five days without drinking in the past – their large stomachs full of digesting vegetation hold a fair quantity of reserve water. Anyway there wasn't anything I could do about it – no chance of setting up a mammoth saline drip. No, the main thing as so often, was to operate as fast as possible and minimise the stress on the poor creature's physiology. If I could remove the source of the pain, it shouldn't take long for the relieved patient to take all the liquid it needed on board.

'She'll stand it I'm sure – believe me. Goodnight.'

I didn't dare think about anything going wrong, let alone the crises that can appear out of nowhere with even the simplest anaesthetic procedures, as I made my way to the nearest hotel. The last elephant toothache extraction I'd 'done' was the filmed sequence with the model of Mary at Dudley Zoo. Tomorrow it wouldn't be Rob Heyland doing the sweating (produced by an energetic series of press-ups and then application of Evian water aerosol) and the blood wouldn't be Joyce Dean's bottle of Kensington Gore – it would be me on my own with very genuine human sweat and bona fide elephant blood. No director and no retakes. Take one. Action.

Next morning the sun rose into a cloudless eggshell blue sky. The temperature was cool with the faintest of friendly breezes. Perfect weather for the operation. Over the years I've been incredibly fortunate with the weather for out-of-doors surgery. Except for a Père David deer with its eye knocked out and the Icelandic killer whales, the gods have generally smiled on me or rather on my patient and held back rain and wind until the last suture was knotted. I walked down to the promenade to find Sr Crona had prepared a perfect 2-foot thick carpet of straw a few yards from the sea wall. It was the most public ersatz operating theatre I had ever worked in. There was no shelter, no security wall or fencing, nothing – if anything went wrong. Suppose the elephant didn't get up after the operation – what would the Guardia Civil think of a convalescent elephant blocking the public highway perhaps for days? As predicted there was barely a tourist about, but what would it be like if the business dragged on, possibly very gorily, throughout the day or if – don't even think it, lad – the good burghers of Alcudia sallied forth in mid-morning for their *cortados* to find 3 tons of dead elephant waiting for someone to dispose of it. There was no time to lose.

'Bring her out quietly and stand her in the middle of the straw,' I said. The Cronas looked as if neither of them had slept a wink. They went to the truck, opened the doors and for the first time I had a good view of the sick animal. She was huge even for a mature Asian elephant and as they coaxed her, without touching her head, down the ramp, I saw that the few days without food and particularly water had ripped weight off her. No roundness at the right places, skin tight and dry. She eyed me with weary distaste as she shambled into position. Both the Cronas talked to her incessantly and in passionate earnest in a mixture of Italian and circus German.

'Do you think that you can hold her by one ear long enough for me to inject her in the bottom?' I asked. Sr Crona, pale and unshaven, crossed himself and closed his eyes for a moment.

'Si, doctor – I will. I will.' He turned to look up at his towering child. 'Bambino, my little one.' Tears glinted in the light of the low sun as he implored with a terrible passion. 'Just this once, Dio Mio, let me hold you still.' He reached up and took a hold of the elephant's earlobe. She whisked her trunk a little but let him do it. 'Right doctor – do it.' In my syringe I had less than a teaspoonful of golden liquid, a powerful anaesthetic. Mary might still have been alive if Immobilon had been invented then. While the Cronas both quietly muttered Ave Marias, I gently dabbed the elephant's left buttock with iodine and then holding my breath, slapped the 2-inch needle quickly into the muscle. The Italian prayers so far were answered – the great beast remained motionless. I connected the syringe and squeezed the plunger. It was in! No turning back now.

Three minutes later the elephant began to tremble and then ever so slowly sagged at the knees. I like Immobilon in elephants. They don't come crashing down to the ground, rather they act as if they are made of rubber and someone has just pulled the plug and deflated them. She collapsed on to her brisket with her body more or less in an evenly balanced position. Perfect. I hadn't got a team of burly zoo keepers with ropes to start pulling her around. Mary had lain flat out on one side and the pressure on the underneath lung had been the basic cause of the hypostatic pneumonia. Quickly I checked breathing, pulse, mouth colour and capillary circulation. All was well. Thick veils of foul-smelling saliva hung from the corners of her mouth. It was time to put in the gag and have a feel. There isn't much room inside an elephant's mouth and what there is is mainly occupied by the massive grinding teeth. But I have a small hand and it slipped over the bulbous tongue very cautiously. Even under anaesthetic the jaws might move together slightly by reflex. If, at such a moment, my fingers were between two molars, they would be ground instantly to a bloody paste. I at once came upon the cause of the trouble.

A large tooth in the right lower jaw had erupted at an abnormal angle. It was sitting diagonally in the jawbone. The gum at its base felt spongy and grossly swollen. Dental trouble sure enough and on a grand scale. With a torch I could just see the offending molar. It looked at its crazy angle like the prow of an old sailing ship wrecked and reared up on a reef of pink coral. Twenty years earlier, Mary's tooth with its abscess had been embedded in a normal position in the jawbone – like an iceberg with nine-tenths of its bulk beneath the surface. This nasty-looking molar might with a bit of luck be easier to remove. Elephants have a total of twenty-four tooth buds when they are born, so twenty-four teeth have to do them for all their lives. They have four in use at any one time, two above and two below grinding together like millstones. As the two front teeth are worn down they gradually move forwards along the line of the jaw and eventually fall out. The pair behind then take their place. When the last pair of twenty-four fall out, the elephant in the wild starves to death. Not so, of course, in a safari park or zoo where boiled rice, molasses, sugarbeet pulp and chopped hay will be provided. The oldest Asiatic zoo elephant on record lived to be 77 years, far longer than most of their fellows in the wild survive on average.

I had my burglar's tools sterilising in a bucket of disinfectant. With the gag firmly in place and held by Sr Crona and his wife shining the torch, I sprawled on my stomach in the straw and slid the bodger and a chisel into the mouth. Like a miner on a very narrow seam, I clinked away at the rock-hard tooth where it emerged from the gum. I needed a place of purchase for my jemmy. When I had banged away for two or three minutes I withdrew the chisel and put the jemmy into the niche I had made. Bang! I clouted it home hard with the bodger and then started to lever with all my strength. There was a crack like the breaking of green wood and at once the tooth came away in a torrent of pus and blood. The smell was appalling. Triumphantly I pulled the rotting molar, the size of a house brick, out of the elephant's mouth. The Italian couple at first gasped and then almost went hysterical with joy. The hole in the jaw was big enough to thrust my fist in – I washed it out with several litres of warm water and Tego antiseptic and then gave the unconscious elephant a large shot of tetracycline antibiotic into its shoulder. The heart and lungs were still functioning normally as I listened with my stethoscope. Now for the magic bit. I filled a syringe with a teaspoonful of blue antidote and injected it through a fine needle into one of the veins on the back surface of an ear.

'Stand back!' I shouted – a knot of holidaymakers and locals had gathered round. 'She'll be up in thirty seconds.'

Like clockwork, half a minute after the antidote injection, the elephant gave a deep sigh, flapped an ear and in a cloud of straw dust gracefully rose to its feet. It was just past 7.30 am. The tourists put up a ragged cheer and the Cronas hugged one another and started weeping with relief. Alcudia in all its history, I am sure, has never witnessed a finer sight than that elephant standing by the water's edge on such a bright and beautiful morning.

'Has the pain gone doctor?' asked Sr Crona, coming over to me and giving me a powerful hug. Certainly the elephant's face seemed to have lost some of its tenseness and desperation but it still looked mighty weary from loss of sleep.

'We will soon see, Signora,' I replied. 'Fetch a bucket of warm water.' The water appeared and was placed in front of the elephant. She looked down at it and slowly dipped the tip of her trunk in and sucked. She hesitated several times in curling the trunk into her mouth but finally did it and released a small quantity of liquid. We could *see* the surprise, the relief, the wonder in her eyes at that moment as the water touched the spot that had been raging with pain for so long – sore it still was, but the agony was gone. She released the rest of the water into her mouth – it still didn't hurt! Quickly she reached for more water. Then more – the bucket was speedily emptied. Bucket after bucket of water was fetched for the thirsty giant and as she replenished herself her expression softened, her eyes rolled and we heard her purr. The purr of an elephant – deep, catlike but amplified a thousand times – is one of the most charming sounds in the world.

'She is happy again!' cried the Italian lady and she put her hand up to the animal's mouth. The elephant nuzzled her just like old times.

'Go to the bar and bring a stack of *ensaimadas*,' I said to Sr Crona. The soft sweet pastries, modelled they say on the turbans worn by the Moorish invaders of Majorca, would be just the thing now for trying out her ability to eat solid food.

A few minutes later the Italian returned with a tray stacked with the newly baked *ensaimadas*. I took one and offered it to the elephant. The 'finger' on her trunk tip grasped it delicately but she was extremely nervous about introducing it into her mouth. Would she, wouldn't she? She jiggled it back and forth and then so slowly pushed it in. We waited. She waited. The *ensaimada* touched the scene of my excavations. It didn't feel bad – in fact it felt pretty good and tasted delicious. The elephant swallowed the sugary confection and greedily reached for the next. The heap of *ensaimadas* disappeared in no time at all, to everyone's delight.

'*Mas ensaimadas*!' Out ran the bar tender with a second ovenwarm trayful and it suffered the same fate. I have never seen happiness and relief so plainly written across an animal's face. It radiated pure joy as it breakfasted. An urgent request for back-up supplies was sent to the next bar down the road and the one beyond that.

'Wash out the mouth with salt and water after feeding for a week and let her rest and get some sleep for a few days before going to Minorca,' I told the Cronas. 'Otherwise, that is that.'

'Miracolo,' murmured the Signora and we all posed for photographs holding the evil-smelling tooth like a football cup. At 8.30 after breakfast (there were no *ensaimadas* left for any of us humans), I set off for Palma and the next plane back to London. As the taxi passed the groves of almonds, olives and oranges, the fields of rich red soil and the broken down windmills, I thought, of course, of another elephant in another place and another time. It was a sort of miracle that the company who make Colmans English mustard had also developed not another condiment but an elephant anaesthetic. Hail Mary, full of grace.

5 A Case of Crabs

I am not generally fishy. That is not to say I don't appreciate a fresh Dover sole and I certainly cook the best mackerel with gooseberries in the whole of Surrey. No, it's the live fish, the fish with problems, the bilious bass or menopausal monk fish that I know little about. In the past, Andrew had devised a humane technique for blood sampling lobsters and I'd removed growths from the occasional prize aquarium specimen. There was even the case at a Dutch zoo where we treated a group of sharks who'd become apathetic and showed swellings in their throats just about where we reckoned a shark might have a thyroid gland, for possible goitre. Doses of iodine and then thyroid hormone did indeed do the trick. Fancy seeing Jaws with what used to be called Derbyshire Neck! But fish, as opposed to marine mammals, really weren't my bag and the situation in our practice where many of the zoos and marinelands that we visit possess often elaborate and beautiful aquaria remained icthyologically inexpert until recently. Now we have one of the most experienced fish veterinarians in Europe, Peter Scott, as our assistant and I have quickly learned from him a number of fine-sounding phrases which might make an impression of suitable gravitas some day as I gaze into a tankful of baleful Piranhas.

'Jolly fine finnage there!' I'll say. It's like chatting to horsy folk about conformation and bog spavins and 'Were you at Hickstead?' – the lingo is all important.

Some years ago I received an unusual call one evening.

'Doctor Taylor,' said a man's voice, 'can you treat crabs?' Crustaceans – the lobster, prawn and shrimp family –

do have a variety of recorded ailments. Like most other creatures they are prey to parasites and bugs of one sort or another, but it's an arcane branch of veterinary medicine to say the least and I wouldn't recommend any young veterinary graduate to set up his plate in Whitstable with the hope of making a reputation out of crabs with rheumaticky joints. But I know where to look up information.

'Well, you know, it's not my field,' I told my caller, 'but you can bring them here in the morning at ten if you like. I'll see what I can do. Perhaps send away material for laboratory diagnosis.'

'Good. So long as I get some treatment started. I'll be round at ten doctor.'

He rang off. Precisely at 10 o'clock the next morning the doorbell rang and I opened the door to find a dapper little man of distinctly military bearing on the step. Middle-aged with a florid face, sparse hair flattened to a shiny pate by Brylcreem, gingery eyebrows over pale blue eyes and a short ginger moustache waxed into needlelike spikes at either side of a beak-like nose, he was wearing a neatly pressed pin-striped suit that was fraying slightly at the cuffs.

'Doctor Taylor? – Mascue, Captain Mascue. Retired.' Said the little man shooting out a gloved hand. 'Came about the crabs.'

I ushered him into the little room which serves both as my study and consulting room for the relatively few clients that I see at home. Definitely an eccentric I thought as he took a seat. What's this character doing keeping crabs? Looks like a bounced cheque, going on past experience.

'Now, Captain', I said, 'what can I do for you? You understand I'm not an expert in shellfish.' The blue eyes bored into me as he fished in a pocket and brought out an unusual cigarette case made out of flattened rifle cartridges.

'Mind if I smoke?'

'No, go ahead.'

'These crabs, doctor,' he lit a Black Russian and carefully replaced the spent match in the matchbox, 'they're not crab crabs. They are . . .' He gave a quick checking twirl of the moustache spikes. 'They're beetles.' Nonplussed for a moment, I suddenly comprehended.

'Oh you mean crab-*lice*.' Mascue brushed a speck of ash from one shining brogue shoe and nodded.

'Correct. Beetles.' Lice aren't beetles, though they are insects but I wasn't going to argue zoology.

'Er, what – what animal has got the crabs, Captain Mascue?' There are nearly 3,000 species of lice known to science and most are very choosey about which kind of animal they'll live upon. Some specialise in sea-lions, others in chinchillas or porcupines, and there is an odd one called *Haematomyzus* that is only found on elephants and warthogs. I've come across it once in a newly arrived young elephant at the Welsh Mountain Zoo. And, of course, there are the bunch that don't fancy anything much except a meal of human beings. The layman's term 'crab' is generally only applied to one of the two species of louse that affects man – *Phthirus pubis*. Lice are not only highly selective generally about which animal they live on; they go further and are terribly fussy about *where* they live on their host. Mr *Phthirus pubis* hangs in pubic hair while the other louse, *Pediculus humanus*, comes in two subspecies, one Mr *P.h. capitis* that inhabits head hair and Mr *P.h. humanus* – denizen of body hair. Even stranger, the head lice of man have evolved into different races which are distinctly adapted in claw shape and otherwise to life on the heads of the various human races. There are those which have claws specialised for grasping the hairs of negroes and there are American, European and Chinese varieties. Virtually every kind of mammal and bird has its sort of louse (and fish have lice too – I've got a louse taken from a tuna fish in South America in a bottle on my desk that is as big as an acorn). My visitor gave a short, possibly nervous cough.

'The animal is our pet monkey, Goebbels. He's in the car. But . . .' Mascue hesitated and turned to look out of the window.

'No trouble with lice – crabs if you like – these days, Captain,' I interjected, 'we can clear them up quick as a wink with modern aerosols and powders.'

He turned back to look at me again and sucked deeply at his cigarette. 'Good. Good. But . . . it's not as simple as that. You see it's not just the monkey. It's, well, it's us. Mrs Mascue and, well, me. We've caught them too.'

'Still no problem,' I said, smiling I hoped reassuringly. 'Just as simple to eradicate in humans. The chemist or your doctor can recommend a louse powder. And if the monkey is the source – it does occasionally happen because they are after all primates and some lice will cross from one species of primate to another and survive for a while – well, it's best to treat you all simultaneously.'

Lice aren't common in monkeys but I'd had cases over the years.

'Doctor – these lice – you don't understand. They are *crabs*. Our GP says so. He's seen them on both me and the lady wife.' He stubbed out the cigarette and immediately pulled out the cigarette case again and lit another. 'The point is . . . the little blighters, the crabs are in the same place on the both of us – and Goebbels!'

'Where?'

'To be perfectly frank – in our lower parts.'

'Your pubic regions?'

'Yes – that's about the size of it.' Mascue's red face was partly masked by dense wreaths of Sobranie smoke – 'and nowhere else.'

Crab-lice in monkeys – I'd never heard of that occurring. But it was perfectly possible. I decided not to speculate as to how the transmission from man or woman to monkey or vice versa might have taken place. 'Let's have a look at Goebbels,' I said. 'Bring him in.' Mascue went out to his car and came back with a parrot cage in which sat a grumpy-looking male rhesus monkey.

'He's as nice as ninepence,' said his owner releasing the animal, 'wonderful nature. Mess mascot when we were in Aden.' Goebbels glowered and raised his eyebrows at me in challenge.

'Why do you call him Goebbels?' I asked.

'Look at his face – see the resemblance?'

'Yes, the monkey did have features remarkably similar to those of the Nazi propaganda minister.

'And he does the Nazi salute – Sieg Heil, Goebbels! Sieg Heil!'

At Mascue's command the monkey raised his arm, hand stiff and straight.

'Quick march, Goebbels! Quick march!' said the little man and the monkey at once goose-stepped, still glowering, up and down my desk in the most comical fashion.

'Can you hold him, Captain, while I look at these "crabs"?'

Mascue deftly put a full-nelson on Goebbels while I cautiously straightened the monkey's legs and peered at its groin. Sure enough, small grey crab-like creatures, lice, were clambering about among the sparse hairs.

'See what I mean doctor?' said Mascue, 'and that isn't all of it!'

I took a magnifying glass and a pair of tweezers and selected one of the parasites for bottling in preserving fluid.

'You see, our GP, Doctor Prendeville, has shaken Mrs Mascue rigid. When she asked him where the crabs could have come from he said – well, to be frank again – he said by, er, having relations – you know – intimate relations. He doesn't know about Goebbels having them!'

True, human crab-lice are normally transferred by sexual contact (the romantic French call these very unromantic animals 'butterflies of love'), and the recent rise in crab-louse infestations in man has paralleled the ascending curve in the incidence of venereal disease. Mascue stared out of the window again as he spoke now.

'And that has caused Mrs Mascue to put me on a charge. You see I went with my brother-in-law on a jaunt to Amsterdam last month – you see the picture?'

I saw the picture. The good wife was now accusing her spouse of having brought back from the fleshpots of the red-light district behind the Dam where ladies sit in windows like sides of beef in a butcher's shop, these tiny creepy-crawlies which had then somehow spread to Herr Goebbels when the Mascues petted and played with him. But the key question to my mind was – were these lice the human 'crab' species? The GP, seeing the parasites alive and well and living in Mr and Mrs M's nether regions, automatically assumed they were *Phthirus pubis*. The only things that wandered about human pubes were 'crabs' – end of story. Reach for the prescription pad and write R. Gamma benzene hexachloride. I squinted through the glass at the parasite I had taken from Goebbels. It was a louse all right, but which species? Identification of such brutes is the field of a parasitologist. Lice were lice to me. I'd long ago forgotten what I'd learned in parasitology lectures at university. They were easy to kill with modern chemicals – who needed to know their proper names?

'This might be some help,' Mascue said, pushing a small pill box that he'd taken from a pocket across the desk towards me.

'There's a couple of dead ones from me in there!' Inside the pill box I found two minute corpses identical as far as I could tell to the ones from the monkey. I remembered how the Spanish explorer Cortes had witnessed the poorest Indians bringing bags of lice, the harvest of their bodies, as tribute to the great Montezuma. I put all three lice in a specimen bottle of alcohol and gave Mascue a supply of Quellada shampoo.

'Give Goebbels a bath once a week in that,' I said,

'meanwhile I'll have the lice identified at the Natural History Museum – they may well not be human crab-lice.' Mascue's ruddy face brightened and he gave me a glimpse of a gold molar as he smiled.

'In which case the lady wife will have no cause to keep me in the glasshouse?' he said.

'Absolutely. *If* they are something else,' I replied and we both laughed diffidently.

The report of the examination by the museum's louse expert arrived by post ten days later. It simply said, 'Three lice submitted for identification – all confirmed as *Neohaematopinus sp.*' Now that was a name I'd never heard of before and it certainly wasn't any sort of louse normally found on humans, nor for that matter on monkeys. Captain Mascue will be chuffed when I tell him, I thought, and what's more a letter for his GP should put him in the clear with his Mrs. Dusting off a thick tome on systematic parasitology, I looked up friend *Neohaematopinus*. To my amazement I found him to be a louse that lives on squirrels. Captain and Mrs Mascue and Goebbels had been infested with a most unlikely parasite to be found on primates. I telephoned Mascue with the good but rather unusual news. He was obviously deeply relieved and begged me to send the letter to his doctor without delay. I got the impression that he was still in hot water over the Amsterdam trip and the coincident louse affair.

'You don't happen to have a pet squirrel in the house, do you?' I asked him. It was an unlikely long shot.

'Good Lord, no!' came the reply. 'But the spinney at the bottom of our garden is full of them. Nice little grey fellows. Goebbels gets on with 'em like a house on fire. He spends his afternoon, when the weather's dry and the lady wife is doing a spot of gardening, sitting up in the trees playing with them.'

'So that was it! The squirrel lice had invaded the Mascue household carried from the spinney by the rhesus monkey. They had managed to live and perhaps breed at least for a short time on unnatural hosts. Untreated they probably wouldn't have persisted long, becoming homesick for squirrel fur.

'Better stop Goebbels going up into those trees in future,' I said to the Captain after he told me that the monkey now seemed free of parasites.

'You can rest assured of that, Doctor, and thank you so very much. You don't know how grateful the lady wife and I are that you sorted out the mystery.'

I could imagine. 'By the way,' added Mascue lowering his voice, 'it's just as well. Because the brother-in-law and I had one hell of a rave-up in Amsterdam!'

Before efficient anti-louse preparations were invented, folk put up with or even valued their body lice as signs of good health and virility. They still do in certain backward areas of the Middle East. For an idea of what thoroughly verminous folk were like, I shall leave you with a late thirteenth-century writer who described a captured mongol army thus:

> Their eyes were so narrow and piercing that they might have bored a hole in a brazen vessel. Their stink was more horrible than their colour. Their faces were set on their bodies as if they have no neck. Their cheeks resemble soft leathern bottles, full of wrinkles and knots. Their noses extended from cheekbone to cheekbone. Their nostrils resembled rotten graves, and from them the hair descended as far as the lips. Their moustaches were of extravagant length. They had but scanty beards about their chins. Their chests, of a colour half black, half white, were so covered with lice that they looked like sesame growing on bad soil. Their whole body, indeed, was covered with these insects and their skin was as rough grained as chagreen leather, fit only to be converted into shoes.

What would the dapper Captain Mascue, retired, have made of an army such as that?

6 Blowpipes

I could do with a friendly headhunter. The sort of fellow who, with his long blowpipe and tiny arrows dipped in the poison that exudes from the skin of a slowly roasted arrow-frog, can with deadly accuracy hit a monkey or bird high in the Amazonian tree cover. He would be perfect as my assistant now that anaesthetic darts, fired or should I say puffed from light metal blowpipes, are much in vogue again in the zoo world. They've been around a long time but have only recently been developed into more sophisticated professional instruments. Strong, light alloys have reduced the risk of damage to the pipes as one stalks a patient through woodland or between the bars of hospital cages. The powerful grip of a chimp or orang-outang who suddenly made a grab at them was sufficient to pinch together or, not all that infrequently, tie in knots the earlier blowpipes much to the vet's embarrassment and the ape's entertainment. The range of the weapons has been increased by substituting a small portable carbon dioxide gas bottle or footpump linked by plastic piping to the tube for human lung pressure. The advantage of the blowpipe as against the dart gun is, as you might imagine, silence – less alarm among the animal targets than occurs after the sharp report of gas or blank cartridge-fired pistols and rifles. And the light darts with their fine needles are less traumatic to the tissue of small animals such as squirrels, monkeys, or ring-tailed lemurs. The disadvantage is the limitation on the size of flying dart and hence the volume of injectable liquid which can be projected by a blowpipe, although with modern drugs of high concentration and activity we still have plenty of scope for tackling reasonably large creatures. Blowpipe syringes bigger than 3 cc volume are at present not a realistic proposition and the ones we normally use are only 2 cc – less than half a teaspoonful. Bear in mind, though, that such an amount of, say, etorphine would knock out a gnu or, if it were lyophilised ketamine, would render an adult chimpanzee unconscious for half an hour.

Blowpipes are, of course, just hollow tubes. You could make a perfectly effective one out of a length of curtain rod or central heating tubing bought at the local DIY store without any modification. However, as soon as you buy that length of tube with the intent of puffing life-saving plastic darts down it, it becomes instantaneously, as if by transubstantiation at the moment that the store-keeper takes your cash, a prohibited weapon for which you must have not only a fire arms licence but also a special permit from the Home Office. This latter arm of government has never been able to grasp the ridiculous nature of its ruling on this subject (other countries such as the USA are far more enlightened). A tube is a tube or is it? How would they set about prosecuting a vet who happened to have a length of copper tubing lying about the garage? When is a tube not a tube but a prohibited weapon? After all, the tube is nothing without the darts. And the darts are in themselves less dangerous than the much heavier metal darts played with in pubs – without a weapons' licence. They are to all intents and purposes, and can easily be made from, ordinary plastic hypodermic syringes and there's no law about possessing those. And the darts become dangerous only when filled with drugs – but those are all controlled under the Medicines Act and the Dangerous Drugs Act, etc., etc., and are legally held by a veterinary surgeon in any case. It boils down to this in practice. A plumber with miles of central heating tubing in his possession is not breaking the law. A zoo vet with one foot of central heating tubing in his possession, without the appropriate permits, which take months to acquire, *is*.

Would that the Home Office applied such enthusiasm to the control of shotguns – weapons which virtually anyone can obtain with little trouble, and which with sawn off barrels really are frightening things. When I reflect on the surrealistic attitude of civil servants in this matter, I begin to wonder if they realise that the aim of the vet is the relief of suffering and treatment of disease, not membership of the assassination squads of the KGB.

When we first became interested in blowpipes and before the Home Office got excited about lethal curtain rods, I experimented with their use at Belle Vue Zoo. The most complex bit of the equipment is the syringe which expels its contents on hitting the animal by air pressure, as soon as a tiny plastic collar blocking the side firing needle is pushed back by penetration of the skin. That plastic collar, no bigger than a match head, is both crucial and also the Achilles tendon of the whole device. I showed Matt Kelly how it all worked one day in his office by first filling the projectile with ink, fitting the special needle with the obstructing bit of plastic in place and then pressurising the contents by pumping in air behind the rubber plunger of the dart through a non-return valve. Putting the dart into one end of the blowpipe I handed it to the Head Keeper.

'Now first let me make an animal,' I said. There was an empty plastic bag among Matt's garbage and this I filled with water, closing the top with string. This 'body' I dumped in the sink. 'Go ahead Matt – blow like you're one of King Billy's pipers!' The genial catholic grinned, raised the blowpipe, pointed it at the bulging bag and blew a mighty blow. Quicker than the eye could see the dart flew 20 feet and struck home with a barely perceptible hiss. We opened the bag and poured out the water – it was stained an inky blue.

'Kelly, the silent killer of Cork,' declared my friend proudly.

'And the Matt O'Grosso,' I added. Matt didn't get the joke. The blowpipe functioned splendidly when we had our first opportunity to use it on a live animal. A spider monkey with a broken finger didn't realise he'd been darted, so light was the impact and fine the needle. And the system is economic into the bargain. Gas cylinders and charges for the dart guns imported from the USA are expensive – air comes considerably cheaper.

What I don't like about the blowpipe syringes, however, is the need to pressurise them after loading them with the chosen drug. I regard it as a considerable risk that a syringe might spring a leak or burst when under pressure. If the chemical inside were, say, a powerful narcotic it could be sprayed into the eyes, nostrils or mouth and be rapidly absorbed with disastrous results. There are also other potential pitfalls as I found out one day when Matt and I were preparing to blowpipe a sick Thompson's gazelle. One week before the incident which I am about to relate, the Head Keeper and I had had a furious argument. It concerned the common practice of pinioning birds to stop them flying away. A group of Cuban flamingoes and some pelicans had just been delivered to the zoo and Kelly feared that they might quickly try skedaddling back to Cuba, or at least as far as the roof of Manchester Town Hall.

'They got the flighty, wanting-to-be-away look in their eyes,' he muttered, shaking his head knowingly. 'One of these fine mornings ye'll see one stick a toe in the air to feel the run of the wind and they'll be off like Murphy's donkey – ye'll best be pinioning em, me boyo!'

'I'm against pinioning,' I replied, 'we'll feather clip them instead.' It was Matt who showed me how to pinion a bird. No anaesthetic, two quick cuts with a sharp knife through a joint and roughly one-third of one wing was amputated. The birds seemed to stand the primitive surgery remarkably well but it was undeniably barbaric. Even nowadays with the use of local and general anaesthetics (and some folk still don't use anything) I cannot defend the mutilation of an animal for the purpose of stopping it from running away. Clipping the flight feathers on one wing is humane, painless and works well enough but it does have to be repeated when the plumage regrows.

'Augh. Feather clipping! Waste o time!' Matt retorted. 'Namby-pamby half measures when ye could do the job once and for all!'

'Pinioning is cruel, Matt. It's like cutting off one of your feet to stop you walking to the Longsight pub.'

'Nonsense. Look here. Bird keepers have been pinioning birds since long before you plastered yer first nappy, young sir. These new-fangled ideas 'll have those birds out of here the first windy day that gives 'em a bit of lift. I've seen it happen.' The Irishman's dander was up. His face was becoming puce coloured and his teeth were gritting like chalk on a squeaky blackboard.

'Well, you can go on about it all day if you wish, Mr Kelly,' I said, trying to look as grim as he. 'But I'm the vet here. We're feather clipping from now on and it'll be your job to keep a record of when they're ready for redoing. Please catch up the first one!' Kelly, looking as if he were about to take wing like an avenging angel himself, stamped across the grass towards the drained flamingo pool mouthing things it was probably better not to hear. I took some large scissors from my case. He came back with a flamingo under his arm and relaunched his attack.

'I mean, how many flamingoes have you ever done your way? I've pinioned trillions and never lost one!'

'I'd sooner lose the occasional one rather than hack lumps off the poor devils – anyway the argument is finished. We do it my way.'

'Book learning doesn't make up for experience, I know that.' Matt almost spat the words out.

'I *know* that we're wasting time gassing. Spread the wings for me please. And by the way, it's just crapped down the front of your trousers.' Puce face turning to imperial purple and seemingly struck dumb, the Head Keeper looked over the back of the bird at the slimy green trail wending its way towards his shiny black boots.

Seven days later, our little wrangle forgotten, Matt and I stood by the fence at the paddock range where the small herd of Thompson's gazelle were breakfasting on oats and flaked maize – the same cereals that make the porridge and corn flakes with which many humans begin the day. One of the animals was thinner than the rest and seemed apathetic about food. I suspected it might have a foreign body – a plastic bag or some hay baling twine – knotted up in its first stomach. A half cc of Immobilon in the blowpipe dart promised to be the answer to the problem of catching the animal to examine it without panicking the others into dashing into the fencing and maybe breaking a neck or two. Following my normal practice I first filled a hypodermic syringe with some of the blue Immobilon antidote, Revivon, and put it in a conspicuous place on top of a fence pole.

'There's the blue stuff, Matt,' I remarked, 'just in case there are any accidents.' I operate generally under what the Americans call the 'buddy' system – always making sure that there is someone around who knows where the antidote is and what to do with it if a needle slips. With Immobilon you don't need to actually inject yourself – a scratch of a needle moistened with the drug could be enough in a great ape, such as Homo sapiens, to produce a lethal effect. A number of vets had died in accidents where they were working alone or with people who did not know about the risks or the life-saving antidote which was undoubtedly somewhere in a bottle within a few feet of the collapsed vet's body. And it's the Revivon that is used to bring round the animal you're anaesthetising at the end of the operation or examination. After the antidote syringe was in position I loaded a flying dart with Immobilon, carefully pressurising it while holding it at arm's length with my head turned slightly to one side to avoid any spray if the device burst. Then I picked up the blowpipe and was about to slide the dart into it when Matt gave a sudden loud cry of dismay.

'Mother of mercy, what did I tell you – look at that!' I looked up to see him gesticulating angrily at the sky. A handsome deep red Cuban flamingo, indubitably feather clipped, was flying into the strong breeze blowing towards the Hyde Road. Without too much effort it cleared the high wall and disappeared in the direction of the greyhound stadium. 'What did I tell ye!' stormed the Head Keeper. 'A hundred and fifty quid gone awol because ye damned well wouldn't pinion the cratures!'

With a modicum of chagrin I pulled a wry face but said nothing and turned once again to the job in hand. The dart was in the blowpipe and I took up the stance of a warrior Dayak, the long tube pointed towards the gazelle standing perhaps 15 yards away. I inhaled deeply, put the blowpipe to my lips and blew. The dart hit the animal's rump, discharged its contents and then fell out as the gazelle trotted a few steps at the brief prick. But something was wrong, off key. I sensed it but couldn't at first place it. It wasn't the animal or the point of impact of the dart or the drug dosage. In a flash it came to me – I had felt a tiny drop of cool liquid touch my lips as I blew. Where had it come from? It wasn't raining. The blowpipe had been taken out of a dry box. It couldn't have been my own saliva, could it? A wave of panic swept over me. It was, it could only have been one thing – a globule of Immobilon escaped somehow from the dart. Kelly and his accursed flamingo had distracted me just as the needle point was entering the blowpipe. I'd looked at him and taken my eyes off the sy . . . ringe. Per . . . haps a bit . . . The paddock range of dark red gunnite rockwork and gravel slowly began to move around me. The Immobilon was already in my system. As the fencing and Matt swung round me as if on a giant carousel, the blue antidote syringe rolled along too. Years of fear of the anaesthetic accident with the drug that is 10,000 times more potent weight for weight than morphine reached their climax. And the old fear was the spur that at that moment made me thrust out my hand and snatch the pretty blue bauble from the accelerating merry-go-round. Crashing to my knees I rammed the needle through my trousers into my thigh and squeezed the plunger. Falling back against the fence I could hear Matt Kelly shouting, 'Saints in heaven! – what's up lad? What's up? WHAT'S UP?' He was down beside me slapping my cheeks and ripping at my shirt collar. Oh, how his boots shine I remember thinking – high on a heroin-like trip. The shine is where he's polished the leather 'til it's so thin I can see through it like a pane of glass. Beyond the glass is a wonderous landscape of rolling hills, green like no words can describe and from the hills silver cataracts pour. I can count every bead of silver water if I try – I can see inside any bead if I choose. It's cool and sparkling within the beads of water . . .

The magic landscape disappeared abruptly – Kelly's smacks had made my cheeks smart unpleasantly.

'Ger off!' I grunted groggily. The paddock range was stationary again I noticed.

'Hey you're awake boyo – you're awake!' Kelly sounded distant but obviously greatly relieved. The Revivon was doing its stuff, quickly neutralising the minute quantity of Immobilon that I had absorbed through my lips or the membrane lining my mouth. Within five minutes of collapsing (Kelly told me that what had seemed like hours to me had lasted no longer than that) I was on my feet again albeit with a hangover that would have done an absinthe drinker proud. The Thompson's gazelle on the other hand was flat out. I filled a syringe of Revivon with trembling fingers and gave it to Matt. 'Go and stick this into its ham muscle,' I said. 'I'm in no shape to examine it today. Bring it round now and we'll start again tomorrow.' Looking very shaken himself Kelly brought the little gazelle back to consciousness while I leaned heavily on the fencing. 'I wonder if it was grazing in those green green hills with the silver cataracts,' I said when he climbed back over the fence.

'What are ye on about David?' asked the Head Keeper looking anxiously at me. 'Now come on let's get you back to the office for some black coffee and I'll ring for Doctor Brown to nip in and have a look at ye!'

A day in bed cleared the traces of the chemical from my system though the 'dirty' injection through my trousers set up a mild inflamation which had eventually to be controlled with penicillin tablets. All in all it was a near squeak and it taught me the hard way the dangers of using such drugs with blowpipes. How the drop of liquid escaped I never absolutely determined. The most likely explanation is that the plastic collar on the needle was not a perfect fit and permitted some of the syringe contents to seep out on to the needle shaft. If I had done what Kelly wanted and pinioned those flamingoes it probably would not have occurred. Even with a trace of Immobilon on the needle I would have inserted the dart in the blowpipe without distraction and without touching the rim of the tube which later came in contact with my lips.

'Now perhaps ye'll heed what I say about pinioning,' said Matt when I was operating on the Thompson's gazelle two days later and pulling a tangle of plastic out of its rumen.

'Over my dead body!' I replied.

'Mm, with you and that poip of yours, m'lad, I'm thinking that won't be long now.' The Irishman chuckled merrily and I started stitching up.

7 Doomed Dolphins

The Mediterranean and the Adriatic are dying – certainly their inshore waters are being slowly murdered by over-fishing and pollution. The diminished fish stocks and the untreated raw sewage of thousands of hotels are making a graveyard out of waters that were once famed as the haunts of leaping dolphins. Malta and Cyprus, Sardinia and Sicily were traditionally islands garlanded by sea that was alive with the music and movement of these fabled creatures. Where are they now? Some, a rearguard composed mainly of the deeper water species, are still around though in greatly reduced numbers. The plain fact is that the ocean is sick and it was vividly brought home to me in 1977 when I was called to Italy to investigate a series of deaths in newly caught dolphins of the Atlantic bottle-nosed species. Marinelands up and down the Adriatic coast and a few on the Mediterranean side were catching the cetaceans in their own waters rather than importing from Florida or the Gulf of Mexico. But no matter how carefully they tended the new arrivals, disaster seemed to strike inevitably within the first few days or weeks. 'A plague, a visitation has struck us,' an Italian biologist declared to me on the telephone. Some talked of a mysterious virus on the rampage, others that the fish on which the dolphins were fed must have been feeding on poisonous 'red tides' of algae before being netted. Andrew and I had examined a number of ill and dead dolphins from the area. Pickled material and bacteriological swabs were arriving by post in Keighley and Lightwater every day. But we could find no disease common to all cases, no evidence of a new bug like the Legionnaires' disease organism or an exotic virus. Poison seemed unlikely. The dolphins we examined were suffering from a variety of complaints – pneumonia, enteritis and septicaemia – and the causes appeared to be common bacteria, well known to science, but often very resistant to normal antibiotics.

What was particularly noticeable was the high incidence of disease in animals that had been caught for only a few days. As soon as they were dropped into a marineland pool, no matter how thoughtfully designed and often with water as clear as blue gin, they gave up the ghost. The same species of dolphin taken in the waters around the United States were at the same time completely unaffected by the 'Italian curse', even when shipped to Italy. The mother of a dolphin trainer working in Riccione went on record in the local newspaper claiming it was a sign of God's displeasure at the election of a liberal new Pope. A Communist mayor in a nearby town blamed it on radiation leaks from the vessels of the US Sixth Fleet. Certainly by the time we had reached any ailing animal, neither Andrew nor I had had much success in arresting the disease process. All year we were flying in and out of Italy and our recovery rate was consistently and unusually low at around 25 per cent. 'What we need to do is study the disease pattern in wild dolphins particularly in the Adriatic,' Andrew said to me at the height of the crisis. That was where the vast majority of Italian dolphins were coming from. He was right, but how? No chance of an open sea clinic, and killing a sample of dolphins for pathological examination was unthinkable. There seemed to be no solution – just slogging it out with the cases as they arose. We even considered setting up a base in Italy in order to gain time in beginning therapy of new patients, and antibiotics so new that they were only on controlled release to hospitals were obtained by us for trial on the sick dolphins.

Then one day an unexpected opportunity arose to put Andrew's wish into practice. A Swiss client with dolphinaria in Italy rang to say that he had arranged to have twenty dolphins captured by fishermen sailing out of Rimini. What should he do to protect the animals against the pestilence?

'Hold everything till I get down there,' I told him. 'I want to go out with those fishermen and see the animals right from the second they are caught!' He readily agreed and I hurriedly packed The Bag with extra gear and booked a flight to Bologna. I was elated at the prospect of closely observing such a large group of animals from point of capture and then through their first days in a marineland. Perhaps I could pinpoint the factor or factors that were triggering the outbreaks of disease. Maybe there was some unusual stress factor on board the fishing vessels. Perhaps they did something that was never done by the Americans or vice versa.

The three little fishing boats left Rimini at first light. The sea was oily with a languid swell. It wasn't ideal for dolphin spotting but it could have been worse. The same applied to my stomach – it was in an undecided and delicate state that was almost thrown into disastrous disarray when the good-natured fishermen, who didn't speak a word of English, proceeded to breakfast on the way out on fatty white sausages washed down with red wine. By busily sorting through my instruments I avoided watching them. Twelve miles or so from the coast, a look-out in the bows of our boat sighted a school of dolphins doing nothing very much except bobbing lazily in the water. They may have been napping (dolphins can also sleep while actively swimming) or basking after their first meal of the day. The three boats spread out to encircle the dolphins with a half mile of fishing net in much the same way that I was used to off the Florida Keys. As a watery sun at last broke through the light sea mist I counted about thirty dolphins, bottle-nosed for sure, encircled by the net. Two hours later exactly twenty of the sleek great creatures were lying on foam mattresses in the deck wells of the three boats. The fishermen were fairly gentle in handling the dolphins but they didn't seem to have the same understanding of them that is always found in American catchers. I had to show them by gestures how to position the sea mammals for easy breathing, how to keep damping them down and the importance of avoiding even slight damage to important areas such as the 'arm pits' where the flippers join the trunk, the tips of the beaks and the edges of the tail flukes. They followed my instructions with genial goodwill and there was much singing and consumption of more red wine and sausages as we turned for home. The morning's catch would pay well – 800 US dollars apiece was the bargain they had struck with my Swiss friend. As soon as the dolphins had been brought aboard I had begun examining and sampling them. I identified each one by a drawing showing distinguishing blemishes – a scar here, a dent in a dorsal there – and then checked condition, colour, teeth, eyes, smell of the breath from the blowhole and looked for significant injuries. It was at once obvious that only a few of the animals were in plump and perfect condition. Some were downright thin. Others had opaque eyes or halitosis. That was distinctly odd. Finally I took a blood sample from the tail of each animal. This was the key test. As soon as we landed I wanted to get the blood to a laboratory for basic analysis without delay. Back in Rimini the boats unloaded the dolphins on to the quayside where two long lorries carrying individual foam-lined crates were waiting along with dolphinarium staff who would supervise the final stage of the journey to the dolphin pools. I went along on the back of one of the lorries. It all seemed very much the same as in Florida – no major stress apart from the very fact of being captured, but that was the same in the Adriatic, the Bahamas or off the Everglades.

The twenty dolphins were safely delivered to their destination by 1 o'clock in the afternoon. By the following morning when I inspected them, most were ill, few would accept food and one or two looked likely to die within the day. So it turned out. By the end of the week all twenty had gone – decidedly and stubbornly dead despite the most intensive treatment I could muster. Grossly tragic as the incident was, I learned two surprising and very important facts which essentially explained the nature of the 'plague'. First, the blood samples which I took just after capture on board the fishing vessels revealed the existence *at that time* of disease in the bodies of all the dolphins. Secondly, at autopsy each sad cadaver revealed infected and malfunctioning organs often of a kind we had rarely seen before in this species. Kidney stones, breast abscesses, chronic pneumonias and diseased testicles – every dolphin had one or more such lesions. From the tissues we grew in culture all the sorts of bacteria associated with sewage dirt and pollution in general – ubiquitous germs of no special distinction but, as with so many bugs in countries where antibiotics are on free sale without prescription, resistant to such medicines. My conclusion was and remains that the wild dolphins of the Adriatic, riddled with disease, are doomed to early death. The stress of capture simply accelerated existing inflammations of lungs, kidneys or whatever and death came just a little quicker. One day soon there will be no more dolphins in the Mediterranean or Adriatic Seas. It won't be because of some strange or deadly new virus. It will be because we, us human beings, are steadily killing the water – choking it to death in a very old fashioned way.

8 Bits in Bottles and Bags

Talk about the post-mortem, the autopsy, the necropsy – call it what you will – and many people wrinkle their noses.

'Bit ghoulish that' or 'shutting the stable door after the horse has bolted', or 'My Augustus is crazy about animals, wants to be a vet but starts to retch when the mere idea of cutting up dead bodies is mentioned' – these are common reactions. In essence, of course, the well-conducted autopsy is a voyage of discovery that both pushes forward the frontiers of medical knowledge and allows one an astounding and intimate view into the miracle of biological creation and the life and livelihood of a piece of self-duplicating and self-repairing machinery more complex and brilliant in its design than any product of Silicone Valley, USA. The post-mortem isn't butchery with a university degree or morbid curiosity in a white coat – I regard it as a mixture of detective work and applied biology, a kind of archaeology – digging among the ruins of a once teeming and prosperous city of cells, cells whose range of jobs were even more varied and colourful than the occupations of the artisans, soldiers, nobles, and whores who populated Pompeii. It isn't a particularly risky business probing about inside individuals which may have died of infectious disease provided one takes basic precautions. In nearly thirty years of pathological examinations on everything from human beings to killer whales, I haven't once picked up so much as an inflamed finger although the knife has slipped or the gloves leaked on the odd occasion. Queasy I was when I looked inside my first cadaver – it was a worm, and not feeling up to the initial unzipping of the creature (I was 12 or 13 years old, I believe) I got Geoffrey Greenwood, a friend from down the street, to do it. But how do you cope with animals which have been dead for days without benefit of refrigerator or even ones that have been exhumed, folk ask. Isn't it, to say the least, rather odorous? Yes, it certainly can be – examining stranded whale corpses that may have lain on a beach in the hot sun for days before discovery, for example, but I developed the simple knack of switching to mouth-only breathing when working in such conditions long ago.

Extracting useful information from an autopsy requires a good and disciplined knowledge of pathology, experience and the existence of certain essential back-up services – laboratories for microscopic analytical work, and so on, but the adventure with scalpel and naked eye, the post-mortem itself, is the on-stage drama. What sort of things might one be hoping to glean from an examination done on, say, one of the Italian dolphins mentioned earlier? We proceed in an orderly fashion, making notes as we go along just like any properly conducted sightseeing tour. First, of course, there is the outside, the skin and its appendages. I hunt for signs of new or old injuries. I often come across healed shark bites, the scars left by that parasitic fish the lamprey and sometimes, yes, holes or furrows of gristly tissue that mark the spot where a 'sportsman' with a rifle took a potshot at the swimming dolphin. Skin diseases of many kinds can be found in dolphins and range from rashes caused by measles-like viruses to rare funguses.

In the mouth many things can go wrong – I remember a very old great-grandmother of a dolphin found dying in the Severn with cancer of the roof of the mouth. But it's in the mouth that we have the opportunity to determine the exact age of the patient by taking out a tooth so that wafer thin sections of it can be examined under the microscope to give a very accurate birth date. Above, the brain is especially interesting in dolphins. Here heavy metals such as mercury accumulate when chemical pollution of the ocean, like the Baltic, occurs. Dolphins are usually long-lived and at the top of the food chain; mercury and other insidious poisons can cause havoc in such species so that a bit of brain taken for chemical analysis will tell us much about the state of the environment during its life. We may also find flukeworm eggs in the brain – they can cause serious damage to the central nervous system, but no one yet knows exactly how they arrive there. Getting at the brain is a most arduous phase of the autopsy and must be done quickly after death to minimise putrefactive change. On down the neck, what there is of it in dolphins, pausing to admire the way in which the larynx clips into the bottom of the blowhole mechanism – a unique feature of cetaceans that keeps the food and air passages completely separate and means that dolphins can never choke on a bit of food that 'goes down the wrong way'.

The lungs are very special in creatures that can dive deep, stay down for long periods and then rapidly surface without getting 'the bends' – the anatomical modifications that permit this wizardry are now under your fingertips. Lung disease is common in these aquatic mammals – signs of abscesses, pneumonia or bronchitis are quickly identified. Parasitic worms often live down here too – especially in the lungs of the little porpoises that frequent the British coastline. While in the chest cavity, the other major organ of interest is, of course, the heart. It isn't unknown for 'coronaries' to hit bottle-nosed dolphins – the blood vessels are arranged very much on the human pattern and have to be checked out. Now is the time to take an uncontaminated sample of heart blood for the bateriologists to work on – it may contain microbes if septicaemia is around. Passing beyond the obliquely angled and very muscular diaphragm we find ourselves in the abdomen. The chemical factory of the body, the liver, takes a lot of the strain in many cases of illness. By feeling, cutting and looking at it – comparing it with the normal liver – we seek the tell-tale 'nutmeg' appearance of chronic heart trouble, the spider's web of white that signifies cirrhosis (rarely due to alcoholism in dolphins!), or the fuzzy yellow patches that may be associated with poisons of certain types. Bits of liver are put into formaldehyde for the micropathologist and others go into the deep-freeze for chemical analysis. Here we may learn how much agricultural pesticide drained down from field to river to sea to fish was taken in by the animal over the years.

Now a trip within a trip – open the stomach (more complicated in a dolphin than a man because it has three compartments). You've a good chance of finding something out of the ordinary here in any dolphin, wild or captive. Clusters of tiny grapes that are in reality curious parasites of the stomach wall, junk in the form of ingested foreign bodies – coins, stones, bits of wood and plastic and ulcers; they are all frequently encountered. On and on, we move into the convoluted tube that is a dolphin's intestine. I bet you a pound there's a tapeworm or two in here. Its segments are packed with eggs that are still very much alive – take care not to transfer any on to your skin. Ingested, these invisible eggs can continue their life cycle in a non-dolphin host, such as a man, to develop not into tapeworms this time but instead into potentially far more dangerous cysts that may grow in the brain, liver or other organs. Emerging from the intestine again we can pay attention to other organs and tissues in the abdominal cavity. Pancreas – any sign of inflammation or tumour? Adrenal glands – cut them in half and look for the haemorrhages that signify acute stress or the thinned outer layer that is the result of chronic stress. The bulky kidneys, resembling those of a cow, lobulated like giant brown raspberries, are a clue to the evolution of the dolphin from cud-chewing land animals that went back to the sea aeons ago. We slice them both lengthways – they may contain stones, cysts, abscesses or signs of nephritis.

Not far from the kidneys we meet the sex organs. Count the little white scars in the ovaries – that will tell you how many, if any, pregnancies a female has had. Samples of the testes are useful for research into reproduction patterns – take and label some and send them to Sir Richard Harrison at Cambridge. Open the bladder – it's not likely but there may be a stone or a polyp in there. Draw urine in a syringe for several tests including looking for abnormal crystals. Finally we must go over the body muscles carefully. The almost black tissue is unlike that of other mammals because of the extra amount of pigment it carries for extra oxygen storage while diving. Let the scalpel seek for evidence of trauma, bruises, the pale fingerprints of vitamin E deficiency or the pockets of gas that may betray the invasion of the fast acting gas-gangrene germ. A bit of real luck would be to dig out the scrap of bone that lies deep in the muscles at the rear of the body and which is all that is left of the hind legs and pelvis of the dolphin – another significant souvenir of the royal progress of evolution. Finished at last with all the bits in their bottles and bags and properly labelled, there is only the scrubbing up left to be done. As I run the water and disinfectant over my hands I frequently take time to reflect on the wonder of what we have just witnessed. Life is indeed, as Napoleon declared to his doctor on St Helena, 'a fortress which neither you nor I know anything about.' No, post-mortems are not morose and aimless guddlings about in one's failures.

9 Killing with Kindness

The vast army of wild animals no less than their human counterparts march on their stomachs. Over the years, travelling across the world I have sampled raw shark meat that has been pickled in its own high content of urea by simply burying it in beach shingle, have been served canapés of salted wood-lice, sweet witchity grubs, bumble-bees in honey and ants in chocolate and have cooked locusts, worms and rattlesnake. Strange as this human fare may seem, I have also encountered innumerable oddities and eccentricities in the diets of my exotic patients. I have written elsewhere of the seductive charms that Glacier mints hold for wallabies, of a monkey crippled by a monotonous menu of egg flip, of hippos that were carnivorous, ostriches that gobbled jewellery, monkeys that pack their mouths with razor blades and elephants gloriously drunk on overripe medlars. Grub is at the root of many of the zoo vet's problems and I am not referring to that incipient *en bon point* that bears witness to my deep love of Italian cooking! When I began working in zoos in the 1950s, by far the two biggest areas of disease were those of parasitic and nutritional origin. Parasitic diseases have largely been conquered or controlled by the development of safe and effective anti-parasite pharmaceuticals and the routine preventive screening of animals by laboratory tests. The incidence of nutritional disease has likewise been reduced enormously as we have learned more and more about the animals' normal feeding habits and requirements, and brought the scientific compounding of concentrate foods, once only applied to farm animals, into the world of exotic herbivores, omnivores and carnivores. Yes, there's even a crunchy protein-rich biscuit available nowadays for tigers, lions, and so on – very much on the lines of the packeted dry food you may give to your pet tabby.

I don't imagine exotic animal victualling will ever reach the heights of sublime ridiculousness seen in some domestic pet feeding. Tsar Nicholas I of Russia, in 1829, instructed his head chef at St Petersburg that his cat, Vashka, which was born on the day that the Russians won a war against the Turks, should be fed on a daily diet that he considered fit for such a noble animal. Its recipe was as follows:

> Two watch-glasses full of best Beluga black caviar, two watch-glasses full of golden caviar, the above to be poached lightly for three minutes in rich champagne. Then add the finely minced meat of one edible dormouse imported from France and turned until gold in unsalted hot butter, the yolk only of one woodcock's egg and a spoonful of fresh hare's blood. Broil in thick cream the whole. Sprinkle the cooled mixture with chopped chervil and the dried cheese of Sukhumi. Moisten (on hot days) with Brut champagne.

When I demonstrated this dish *for fun* as a historical curiosity on 'Afternoon Club' on ITV in 1984, several people indignantly wrote to complain that the £60 per saucerful per day, which is what I reckoned the Tsar's recipe costs at present, seemed rather steep for *a recommended* regime for the average cat. Folk couldn't afford it! As I say I had *not* recommended it. Feeding dogs and cats on luxury foods anyway strikes me as silly, wasteful, unnecessary and possibly immoral, although similar criticisms can be made of us overfed Western Homo sapiens. In a world where millions of children die of starvation every year, what is one to make of the gourmet restaurant for dogs at the Beach Regency Hotel in Nice where the spoilt canines of the rich and dotty are taken to dine on dishes such as pâté at £2 per dollop, albeit served in a silver chafing-dish.

With more science involved in zoo food kitchens and the passing of men like Matt Kelly who fed animals 'by the seat of their pants' and often without measures or scales, just 'a scoopful of this and a scoopful of that', from bins of bran, oats, maize and linseed together with whatever fruit and veg was in abundance and cheap at the local market, once common deficiency diseases are becoming rare. Big cats given too much raw meat used to develop a bony disease and thyroid trouble because of excess phosphorus and too little iodine and vitamin A, giraffes collapsed in winter from having too little protein and vitamin E in their blood. Nutritional disbalance suppressed reproduction or resulted in abortions or post-natal mortalities, and skin, hair and fur quality were chronically poor when not enough fat or broad enough range of amino acids was built into the daily ration. Nowadays research has changed all that although there are still some species about whose gastronomic needs we do not know enough. These include creatures such as the giant panda, some South American monkeys, certain lemurs and many reptiles.

The majority of feeding troubles that I have to deal with in the mid-1980s are oddball or special cases where, despite the existence of well-formulated and plentiful diets, Murphy's law contrives to keep me on my toes.

Chang-Chang the male giant panda at Madrid developed his taste for Complan, a human invalid wholefood based on milk, when I began treating him for severe bleeding ulcers of the stomach. The bland diet of Complan, rice, honey and baby cereals he found was to his tooth – so much so that he never really relished bamboo again after he was cured. Complan, plain or flavoured, was his delight and so we gave it to him, knowing that its formula was a complete and nutritious food for pandas as well as human beings though lacking in roughage. The latter Chang-Chang would get from the vegetables, fruit and bit of bamboo he also ate. Having looked inside Chang-Chang's stomach when he first arrived through a fibre optic gastroscope and seen the terrible damaged lining, I was not displeased at his new preference for 'pobs' – pandas don't digest their food very efficiently and the idea of chunks of hard raw bamboo rolling about on that delicate lacerated membrane disturbed me. He still, four years later, retains his love of the British made product. Strawberry, chocolate or vanilla – they are all ambrosia to him. He licks his stainless steel bowl free of every minute drop, polishes it with his pink tongue until he can see a perfect reflection of himself, admires his handsome reflection for a post-prandial moment of vanity and then places the bowl at a rakish angle upon his head like a helmet and lies back utterly contented, paws folded across his plump stomach. Chang-Chang in this position always reminds me of some Falstaffian knight in his cups. Though the sloppy panda diet has been beneficial in so many ways, it has one drawback. It encourages the deposit of plaque on the teeth and just as in pet dogs who are fed exclusively on tinned food and don't have chewy raw chunks of skin and gristle to keep their dentures clean, this encrustation can build up to the point where it impinges on the gums, thereby bringing about first gingivitis and later, if unattended, more advanced disease of the tooth socket. Pandas, despite having evolved that marvellous thumb on each forepaw which enables them to grasp bamboo stalks – or should they so wish toothbrushes – do not brush their teeth. By 1983, the vets at Madrid, Liliana and Antonio-Luis and I all began to notice that Chang-Chang's teeth when he yawned (pandas yawn and indeed nap constantly) were becoming yellow and scaly. He had lost the shiny white smile – pandas do possess a charming sly smile – still visible on his stepson Chu-Lin.

With our confidence in panda anaesthesia by now well established (although the Royal Panda Council still has to rubber stamp any decision I make to knock one of the creatures out – usually after the event), I decided to scale Chang-Chang's teeth. In order to do it quickly and efficiently, I proposed to use a modern ultrasonic dental scaling machine rather than the little scrapers and chisels I employed so many years ago on dogs and cats in general practice, and still do with otters who frequently reach the point where their teeth are totally buried under a thick lava-like accumulation of calcified plaque. Pandas being ultra-VIPs in the zoo world, Madrid agreed to purchase £1,000 worth of ultrasonic toothbrush just for the twice yearly dental hygiene sessions on Chang-Chang. For my first essay in the use of the device on anything let alone a giant panda, I needed a demonstration as to the technique. Scaling machines of this type are simple to use and essentially consist of a probe which vibrates to produce ultrasonic waves that crack the deposits of plaque. A fine water jet cools the tip of the probe as it is gently stroked across the tooth surface. It isn't a painful procedure but obviously Chang-Chang would need to be sedated and I didn't want to fumble with the instrument on my maiden voyage round his mouth. I arranged with Mr Parker, my Lightwater dental surgeon, to be present when he used *his* ultrasonic scaler on one of his human patients. The patient, a man in his forties, seemed pleased if at first bemused to act as stand in for a panda. Mr Parker deftly ran the scaler over his teeth and the coating of tobacco stained plaque was whisked away. 'Now,' said my dentist friend, 'would you like to have a go?'

'Mr——doesn't mind?' I asked.

'He's delighted,' replied Mr Parker.

'Yuggle glub glee glub glub,' opined the patient enigmatically in the language only dentists understand, his mouth full of buzzing metal. Now, I've had my hands in some pretty obnoxious places in my time – up to the elbow in giant elephant abscesses, septic giraffe uteri and maggoty washed-up whale carcasses, but the idea of rooting about in a human mouth seemed strangely less attractive than any of these when it came to the point. I could see how the machine worked. It would be simple to apply to Chang-Chang. No need to have a go in that gaping and oddly repulsive human maw. I couldn't be a dental surgeon for *people*, to save the world!

'Er, no thanks,' I said, 'I've seen quite enough. Thank you very much though for the demonstration.'

Some days later with Chang-Chang slumbering under a dose of valium and ketamine mixture, I wedged open the powerful jaws with a pair of rib spreaders designed for thoracic surgery in humans and then set to work with the new machine. Panda mouths are OK by me and I thoroughly enjoyed touching the vibrating probe to Chang-Chang's yellow coated teeth, just as Mr Parker had shown me, and watching the plaque break up and disperse to reveal the shining enamel beneath. With all the scaling done, I brushed the teeth using a new toothbrush and mint flavoured toothpaste (Chang-Chang adores peppermints) and completed the job by rinsing his gums with antiseptic Oraldene. The panda, stirring as he began to come round from the anaesthetic, now had a mouth as shining and sweet as any promised by Macleans or Colgate's advertising blurb.

The bleeding ulcers I had treated in Chang-Chang's stomach were of a quite different character from the ones I sometimes find inside dolphins. Dolphin gastric ulcers are just like those found in middle-aged businessmen and they cause similar symptoms of dyspepsia, abdominal pain and occasional vomiting. It was some years after the first dolphinaria opened in Europe that we identified a probable cause. The role of a chemical called histamine released under conditions of nervous stress had been recognised as important in the chain of events that can lead the human being, subjected to a life of worries, stress and emotional pressure, to develop ulcers. Although happy, active dolphins in marinelands such as Windsor and the Costa Brava didn't *seem* to be under chronic stress, it was something to be borne in mind. Then a very interesting finding came to light. Fish such as herrings, sardines and mackerel, but not salmon, trout or cod, proved on analysis to contain very high levels of an amino-acid, histidine, in their flesh. As soon as the fish die after being caught it was found that the histidine begins to undergo a chemical change, and it changes into histamine. So dolphins who can easily swallow up to 12 kilograms of mackerel a day *might* under certain conditions be ingesting large quantities of histamine. Mackerel has long been known to be the worst fish to feed ulcer-prone human patients – perhaps here was a link between the carefree, athletic, bottle-nosed dolphin and the unathletic, highly pressured city tycoon washing down a Milk of Magnesia tablet with his last glass of port at the business lunch. The theory of high histamine levels in the diet being a major factor in ulcer production in dolphins was born and it is one to which I still hold. Why, you may ask, do you not feed other low histidine species of fish – trout or haddock? The answer is that the dolphins demand fish of a certain size, often to be fed whole, regular high quality supplies must be guaranteed and there is the problem of taste. The dolphins love certain rich fish such as herring and turn their noses up at blander varieties. Spiky, spiny, finned fish such as horse mackerel are unsuitable in general because of the damage they can do to the animal's gullet when fed whole. In Europe and the Mediterranean only mackerel, herring and sprats, among suitable species, can be obtained in sufficient quantity and quality all year round. Faced with a diet restricted to high histidine fish, was there any way round the problem?

The heart of the matter is the change of histidine into histamine after death of the fish. A dolphin killing a fish in the open ocean has no histamine to contend with. Fresh herring or mackerel on the feathered hook or on the deck of a trawler would still contain little of the troublesome chemical, but 'fresh' as meant by the sign on a fishmonger's slab is quite another thing. All fish used in marinelands comes deep frozen. The low temperature reduces chemical changes such as the histidine/histamine coversion, as well as inhibiting bacterial growth and putrefaction in general, stopping the development of enzymes which destroy the vitamin B1 content of the fish, reducing the speed of oxidation that can lead to discoloration and alterations in the fish oils (changes which dolphins can detect in the taste of the food and leads them promptly to reject it), and killing parasites which might otherwise infest the dolphin once ingested. But you can't feed dolphins on blocks of frozen fish. It has to be thawed and as it thaws the temperature of the fish flesh rises and the chemical changes begin again. Although the period between death of the fish and deep freezing can be kept to a minimum by on board flash freezing of the catch, it was the thawing time, the interval between taking a block of fish from the cold room and actually putting it into a dolphin's mouth, that interested me in the late sixties. Were our herrings full of histamine and if so were the thawing techniques used at the time ensuring the dolphins received high daily doses of the troublesome chemical? Over the years I have had so many rows with suppliers of fish to zoos and marinelands – 'We must have the highest quality fish – better than Wheelers Oyster Bar or the Connaught expect,' I had insisted time and time again. 'Humans eat a little fish *cooked* once or twice a week. My animals eat raw fish in large quantities and nothing else 365 days a year.' But the fishmongers could not rid their minds of the idea that this fish was 'animal food' – a term surely synonymous with 'third rate' or 'shop soiled' or 'unfit for human consumption'. 'I don't care whether you give your moggy lights from the butcher or that he seems to thrive on a few penn'orth of fish heads, but my dolphins, sea-lions and the like are every bit as aristocratic connoisseurs of good seafood as members of Whites at luncheon on 1 September! More – they demand the best because their very lives depend on it!' Such exhortations had so often fallen on deaf ears. 'They're only fish themselves aren't they? Animals aren't that *fussy* surely.' The fishmongers must have thought, 'This bloke's exaggerating, must be a bit of a nut.' Whatever their private ruminations they would unfailingly send an initial sample of good fish. Subsequent deliveries would just as unfailingly decline gradually in quality until the animals came out in itchy rashes, got upset stomachs or simply turned up their noses and swam off in disgust. To find at last a few suppliers who understood our needs had taken years of disputes and returned consignments. But still there was the question of the thawing period.

I decided, in 1969, to analyse fish for histamine levels. I bought the best herring from a fish shop on Rochdale market – the sort of gleaming, bright-eyed, firm-scaled, salt-and-seaweed-smelling fish that you and I would buy to make a fine meal with lemon, black pepper and oatmeal. This was 'fresh' as understood by the housewife. Then I took deep frozen herring from our dolphin stock and thawed it in various ways – by leaving it overnight on a wooden board or in a sink of cold water or under running warm water. Each specimen was then analysed at Glasgow University for histamine content. The results were fascinating. The Rochdale market fish, the stuff you and I are most likely to eat at home, contained great quantities of histamine – ten times more than herring thawed in air or cold water. The lowest amount, one-thirtieth of that in the market fish, but still significant, was found in the samples quick thawed in warm water. But I found in further experiments that the histamine content rose rapidly and constantly in all the samples once thawing was completed and the fish stood in buckets waiting for feeding time. So, by fast thawing and only thawing fish in small quantities just before it is needed, I believed we could expect to cut histamine intake and the incidence of gastric ulcers. That is exactly what happened. Cases of gastric ulcer in European dolphinaria were slashed by 50 per cent in the years following my 1969 experiment. We still find some ulcers, of course, and that may partly be because our screening methods have improved with yearly gastroscopic examinations, revealing them often before any symptoms have been noted by the dolphin trainers. Our treatment of these animals has paralleled and been revolutionised by developments in human gastric ulcer therapy. In the early days I was at a disadvantage being unable to put my patients on to bland diets of rice pudding and wholewheat biscuits. They had to keep on with the fatty fish diet. The treatment was a combination of antacids like Milk of Magnesia and stomach pain analgesics secreted in the fish. Not many ulcers healed satisfactorily. Now using cimetidine (Tagamet) and ranitidine (Zantac), the super drugs used for the same condition in people, we can eradicate dolphin ulcers in one or two months.

A unique food fish problem occurred in 1973 when I was called to see some dolphins in Indonesia belonging to a German entrepreneur called Butz. Four bottle-nosed dolphins in a miserable portable pool outside Pontianak in Indonesian Borneo needed help badly. Thank God the days of the travelling dolphin circuses are just about over for good – the conditions which the poor creatures found themselves in wherever they went in South-East Asia from Taiwan to Bangkok were inevitably bad and resulted in an inevitably high death toll. Filthy water, high temperatures, exotic microbes, stressful transports and inadequate pools – they all contributed to the alarming incidence of disease. In those days I was in and out of the Far East, it seemed, every week or two and when I was back in England I was on the 'phone to locations dotted round the South China Sea most days. It was a desperate business – all my portable diagnostic tests and fancy drugs could not make soupy, evil-smelling water clear or find salt where there was none or mend broken pumps in isolated fishing villages or provide shade on sweltering air strips when aircraft were delayed for hours. The dolphins should never have been there but they were and they were always in trouble. A common difficulty was finding supplies of suitable fish when the mackerel and herring, flown out with the dolphins from Europe, were eventually used up. Fresh local species meant parasite risks and the chance of serious food poisoning. Nevertheless, the dolphin circus owners went ahead and fed what was available. Now, in a tree-lined clearing just outside the town of wooden shacks and small plantations of banana, rubber and palm, two dolphins lay floating listlessly in their pool – clearly seriously ill. Two others had died the day before and were lying under sacks nearby. There was the distinctive smell of dead dolphin in the heavy humid air. Gunther, the trainer, stood morosely by the poolside with me and reeled off the long list of troubles he had encountered since reaching the Far East: visa difficulties with Indonesian immigration officials; wages that hadn't come through; his water-testing kit stolen; his assistant, an English girl, gone off on a drug-taking bend in Djakarta and left behind; regular power cuts which meant that the filter only ran on average about four hours a day; the possibility he'd picked up gonorrhoea from one of the local beauties (had I got anything for that please?); obtaining suitable fish for the animals had been a nightmare since the herring had run out and now to cap it all he had lost two animals and looked like losing two more. 'How did it begin?' I asked, after he had finished his lamentations – they were nothing new to me.

'Out of the blue, like a *blitz*, a couple of days ago!' He went on to describe how the dolphins had, despite everything, eaten and worked well up till then. Manila, Taipei, Singapore and Djakarta, without anything more than closed eyes occasionally when the chlorine and dirty water reacted to produce irritating nitrogen trichloride.

'Symptoms?' I asked.

'Oh, they vomit, have severe diarrhoea. And they have these strange twitches. The two that died went into convulsions before they gave up the ghost. It was horrific Doctor.' I watched the two surviving animals jerk from time to time as if given small electric shocks. There was a smear of mustard yellow diarrhoea floating on the water surface.

'I'll need to catch them for examination and blood sampling,' I said, 'but first I think I'll P–M the other two. They will give us a clue, and forewarned is forearmed. In this heat leaving them any longer will make the job even more unpleasant.'

I worked on the two dead dolphins for a couple of hours and to my surprise found myself none the wiser at the finish of the autopsies. No sign of the serious lung, liver or intestinal disease that I had expected. A fast-acting septicaemia was therefore the most likely explanation. The blood samples on the living animals, if I could find a co-operative hospital lab, should reveal that and in any event I decided to lose no time in giving the dolphins intravenous antibiotics. I prepared injections of tobramycin while Gunther and an Indonesian boy who had been hired to do odd jobs unrolled a net with which to catch the sick animals. One very dangerous germ that is widespread in the Far East could be implicated perhaps – the thought chilled me as I washed my hands in a trickle of water from a hosepipe.

Called Pseudomallei, it had wreaked havoc among all kinds of marine mammals at the great Ocean Park of Hong Kong. Difficult to diagnose in life, it leaves few traces at post-mortem for the pathologist. It is common in the soil of many countries of the region and can be deadly for human beings. Many US soldiers died from the bug during the Vietnam War after being wounded by bamboo spikes simply rubbed in soil and set in concealed pitfalls by the Vietcong. It is a germ that can only be countered by certain special antibiotics – hence the tobramycin, just in case.

'If the fish supply is tricky, how do you manage?' I asked the German as we began hauling in the dolphins – they showed no resistance and lay in the nets almost as if with relief.

'Every morning at five I go with Malik here to the fish market and buy what I can.'

'What kinds of fish?'

'Don't ask me their names. Often there is a golden fish a bit like a sardine in shape but with very white meat. The dolphins don't like it. I have also tried pieces of sea bass – that's very expensive. Most of the fish that I can get them to eat are tropical species I've never seen before – some of them with many spines and sharp ridges on them that I always cut off before feeding.'

I began to examine the dolphins, leaning over the side of the low pool where they lay cradled in the net. They weren't in bad condition. Their eyes were bright and their breath smelled sweet. There was, however, this persistent disconcerting twitch that ran down their trunk every thirty seconds or so. Vitamin B deficiency, I wondered?

'Do you give vitamins daily as usual?'

'Oh yes, Doctor. Each one gets five Seatabs every morning.' The American multi-vitamin tablets contained more than enough vitamin B. I took blood samples from the tail of each dolphin and then had them released whereupon they returned to floating again like plastic models of themselves.

It took a long time to find a hospital and then bribe the doctor in charge to get the samples analysed. The facilities were, to say the least, basic and of doubtful accuracy but it was all there was and I was grateful. After half a day of sitting under a jasmine bush outside the low wooden hut that was the laboratory, drinking warm Japanese beer and watching handsome brown and white Brahminy kites gliding across the sky, I got the results. If I could believe them there was no sign of infection or major organ failure.

Great! I thought. The animals have nothing wrong with them except a severe attack of imminent death! I went back to the dolphin pool completely mystified. 'It must be some weird tropical virus.' I told Gunther.

'It is the monkey God who has cursed the lumba-lumba,' Malik the Indonesian boy piped up. A slight, bright-eyed youth permanently wreathed in a cloud of aromatic Kretek cigarette smoke, he thrust a short length of bamboo under my nose. 'See,' he said excitedly in his pidgin-English, 'I show you.'

He took a plug out of one end of the piece of bamboo and shook something out from the hollow interior. What looked like a bit of yellow foliage fell to the ground. I bent down to look at it. It was a large praying mantis, minus its wings which had apparently been neatly cut off close to the joint. Malik picked the mantis up and placed it on the palm of an outstretched hand.

'Gireng, the monkey God's servant. He works for Him, prays to Him – watch!' The Indonesian put the sinister-looking creature on to a flat stone lying on the ground nearby. To my surprise it stayed placidly immobile where it was placed, its long predatory arms folded ready for action. Malik fell to his knees and started searching for something under the plastic sheet surrounding the pool. After a few moments he stood up and showed us a handful of wriggling dark brown grubs each about one inch long. I assumed they were beetle larvae that had been hatched in the wet darkness near the pool base. He took one of the grubs and reaching out over the poolside, touched it momentarily to the skin of the nearest dolphin, hanging in the water like a great grey comma. Then he placed the grub together with one of its fellows which was not introduced to the 'lumba-lumba' on the stone in front of the mantis. The two larvae wriggled furiously and almost immediately the mantis seized the one with which Malik had touched the dolphin. The Indonesian gave a grunt of pleasure and snatched at the mantis again and disentangled the grub from its grasp.

'See,' he cried, 'Gireng serves his master. He shows the monkey God is angry with the lumba-lumba.'

'Fifty fifty chance,' said Gunther, his voice bitter. 'Try it again.' A dozen more times with further supplies brought from under the plastic, Malik repeated the test. And every time Gireng the mantis unfailingly struck at one of a pair of grubs – always that which he'd used to tap on one or other dolphin.

'Now what you think Doctor?' asked Malik triumphantly, as he at last packed the mantis with its reward of a grub back into the bamboo. 'Nothing you can do eh?'

'Mm,' I replied, 'does the mantis always get it right?'

'Always – he took worm-thing (Malik's name in English for the grubs) touched to my mother when she was ill. Sure as hell she died.'

'What happens if the mantis takes the other, the untouched worm-thing?'

'Monkey God let's you get OK again!'

'So according to Gireng those lumba-lumbas will die?'

'Sure Doc – just like my mother and Marilyn Monroe.' There wouldn't be much need for zoo vets or doctors, I thought, if the world at large developed a faith in praying mantises, although there were some of my patients who would be extremely difficult to touch with such an insect. I could imagine someone like Robert, the head of the chimp family at Belle Vue who had a particular liking for live locusts, grabbing the wingless soothsayer and scoffing it before it had time to convey the ordinations of any monkey God. I asked Gunther to show me the food fish and he took me to a little palm-frond hut. A galvanised tub standing on a wooden crate with a hosepipe leading into it served as a sink. Another crate supported a cutting board. The floor was the naked earth, muddy and spattered with fish bits. It smelled bad. A yellow cat was curled up fast asleep in a corner. Pieces of filleted fish lay on the cutting board and a waste bucket nearby was full with the undesirable parts of piscine anatomy – spiky heads, spines, prickly skins and offal.

'I waste far more fish than I feed,' explained the German trainer, 'but just look at some of these scales – they'd rip a dolphin's throat to bits. I skin and bone nearly everything and even then they accept about half of what I offer. It'll give Herr Butz a heart attack when he gets the bill for fish next week.'

I spent no time worrying about the state of Butz coronary arteries back home in Nuremberg – he should have been out in this squalid place seeing what his dolphins were being subjected to.

'Where do you keep the fish after you buy it?' I asked. Gunther led me out and round to the back of the hut. A rusty refrigerator stood in the shade of some banana plants. He opened the door and revealed shelves laden with all manner of brilliantly coloured small fish from the Indonesian waters. I'm not a fish biologist and couldn't give a name to any of them . . . but one fish did look vaguely familiar. Ah yes – Ray Legge's Aquarium at Belle Vue – we had a fine specimen that was of the same shape with a pouting toothy mouth but a slightly different distribution of white spots on the skin and whereas the Manchester fish had a yellow-orange body colour, this one was inky blue.

'What do you call this fish?' I asked Malik.

'Maki-Maki,' he replied. 'Very spensive. Fishermen like to sell to merchants for Japan.'

Japan! *Doctor No*! The James Bond story! It came back to me in a flash. James Bond survived an assassination attempt using a fish poison – from a puffer fish. Of course – this pretty fish with the rather awestruck expression was a puffer fish or, as the Japanese call it, 'fugu'.

'Have you fed any fish like that in the last few days?' I asked. Gunther thought for a moment.

'I think so, maybe one – but you can be sure I would cut off the fins and sharp bits – and I bone such fish as a matter of course.' He took the pretty blue fish with white spots out of the refrigerator and I followed him back to the hut. The trainer started filleting the fish with a small knife.

'See – I do it like this – always I remove anything that might damage the dolphin.' He threw a scrap of meat to the yellow cat that was now awake and it gobbled it greedily. Gunther was certainly removing everything that might do damage – except the fugu toxin. Old memories crystallised into sharp relief. The strange fugu fish restaurants in Japan where specially licensed chefs prepared the flesh of the puffer fish, removing the deadly poisonous parts such as the liver, intestines, sex organs and skin and washing away the dangerous blood and other fluids, and serve it in the form of small raw slivers arranged in exquisite designs upon the plate. I took a minute piece of the puffer fish flesh and pressed it to my lips without eating it. Slowly I felt a faint tingling sensation developing where my lips touched it.

'Hey Doc – look!' cried Malik, as the trainer finished removing four or five long pieces of translucent white meat. He pointed with a look of disbelief at the corner of the hut. The yellow cat lay writhing in grotesque silent convulsions, saliva frothing at its mouth. Forgetting all about the oft-preached rabies risks, I bent down and felt the cat go first rigid and then limp in my hands. Its pupils dilated and glowed pale green, then at once the glow dimmed. The cat was dead as I held it.

'For God's sake stop fiddling with that fish!' I shouted roughly at Gunther. 'You are preparing one of the most poisonous dishes in the world!' The German who had turned to stare at the poor cat dropped his knife and went white as chalk.

'But Doctor, the fishermen sell it for human consumption to Japan!'

'Yes,' I replied, 'quite so. But the Japanese are a strange people. They pay very big money to eat this dangerous fish, but only in controlled fugu restaurants and even so it is the major cause of deaths from food poisoning in that country!'

I recalled not just *Doctor No* but also a fragment of a famous and melancholy Japanese poem – 'Last night he and I ate fugu, today I help carry his coffin.'

'You think Maki-Maki killed dolphins,' asked Malik, as he carried out the dead cat.

'Now I do,' I said, and later was to learn that Maki-Maki was the local name for *Arothron hispidus*, one of the most lethal fugu species. Its English name says it all – the Deadly Death Puffer.

It took a few hours to get through by telephone to England to the London School of Tropical Medicine and then to learn that there is no specific treatment for fugu poisoning. The advice from the toxicologist was to wash out the stomach and give morphine and vitamin B. I couldn't use morphine on the dolphins – it tends to excite rather than ease this species but I at once went to work on the other recommendations. For one of the dolphins it was too late – it died, convulsing just like the cat later the same day. But the other dolphin gradually stopped twitching, became more active and returned to normal after about five days. It was the first and I hope last case of fugu poisoning in a dolphin that I have come across.

'Well Malik,' I said as I packed up to go back to England, 'your mantis got it wrong about one dolphin.' The Indonesian's eyes glittered behind the ever present veil of tobacco smoke.

'No, Doctor, no – he's got it right. This lumba-lumba is also coming soon to death.'

I laughed – but the mantis's prediction was fulfilled. Two weeks later, shortly after returning to Germany, the dolphin died suddenly from an overwhelming acute pneumonia probably caused by a bug picked up in Borneo.

Lions are lovely lazy cats. If you want to see a *real* lion, the sort that pictures, engravings and statues of lions portray, with a mighty mane and glorious colours, seek out a Barbary or Atlas lion, the sort that once inhabited the mountains of Morocco but is now to be seen in all his glory at say Port Lympne Zoo in Kent. At Windsor Safari Park, in 1973, we raised 100 lion cubs on artificial milk without losing a single one. That was when the demand for lion cubs in zoos and safari parks, as well as for reintroduction into the wild, was at its peak. Lions are not difficult beasts to raise or maintain, unlike other cats such as the cheetah who can be very fussy feeders. When a lion or any other big cat for that matter is off colour, I place great importance in prescribing an invalid diet of Steak Tartare à Leo. It is easily digested, tempts feeble appetites and is most nourishing. The recipe is fine, minced, good quality lean meat, beaten whole egg, dried milk and a pinch each of bonemeal, dried yeast and salt. It looks and generally is good enough to eat – for you and me as well as convalescent cats. And therein has lain the problem in the past. Where I've had peaky pumas, languishing leopards or sickly servals in need of a pick-me-up diet, I've directed the purchase of large quantities of best butcher's mince for the feline cuisine. And sometimes, as happened some years ago in an English safari park, the temptation for certain keepers to divert a goodly portion of the meat for their personal consumption has been irresistible. Questions of expense and light-fingeredness apart, what concerned me about the disappearing meat on this occasion was that I suspected my patients – a group of cheetahs recovering from liver disease – were being undernourished, even though we could never actually catch anyone in the act of filching. The answer I came up with was simple and highly effective. I bought a large bottle of violet food colouring and issued it to the big cat keepers stating that it was an important recuperative medicine. A teaspoonful should be added without fail to each dish of steak tartare that was prepared. The effect of the violet colouring on the raw meat was dramatic. It produced an effect which was visually most off-putting (to humans – would you like to eat bright purple meat?), but which didn't bother the cheetahs one bit. Modern research suggests that although cat's eyes may have some anatomical ability to distinguish colours, they need prolonged training to develop colour discrimination which suggests that responses to colour as opposed to shade form no part of a cat's normal behaviour. It wasn't my imagination – the cheetahs definitely put on weight more rapidly after my chromatic prescription.

'How long will we have to give the medicine?' one of the keepers asked me as he eyed a violet dishful with unconcealed distaste.

'As long as it takes till they're fighting fit again,' I answered, 'and can go back on to knacker's meat.' He wrinkled his nose.

'Fair puts you off doesn't it,' he said.

'Absolutely,' I replied, 'that's the idea.'

Keepers are sometimes so blindly devoted to their charges that their obsession becomes counterproductive and even downright dangerous. I have known two cases where male dolphin trainers literally fell in love with particular female animals and had to be dismissed when it came to the stage of a physical relationship which fell into the area of psychosexual disorder and the dark realms of bestiality, a crime under the law. Such incidents are, of course, rare but there are many less extreme examples where an animal attendant has become so tunnel-visioned in his dedication to what he sees as his animal's welfare, that he has achieved the opposite result to that intended.

Tinker was a little Indian elephant brought to Belle Vue Zoo in 1970. She was a frail creature who had been poorly nourished in India, probably on rice balls and little else, but her nature was supreme and gentle and trusting. As soon as she arrived in Manchester she was put into a heated room in the elephant house and I gave her a thorough examination. She was paler than I liked in the eye membranes and mouth and her ankle joints were weak and beginning to sag inwards. In her droppings I found millions of minute blood-sucking worms and her blood sample confirmed that she was very anaemic. Willie, the young assistant elephant keeper, was given the job of rearing Tinker and correcting her nutritional deficiencies. Soya meal, maize and sugarbeat were added to her rice and the mixture was sweetened with molasses. The best apples, broccoli and bananas were saved for her and Willie brought her every day the brown bread that nearly everything at Belle Vue adored, fresh and hot from the bakery. He coaxed her to take spring onions – I have a thing about getting elephants to eat onions which I believe are very good for them – and he spoiled her with boiled sweets and warm milk. Each morning she had warm standing 'bed baths' and was groomed, to an accompaniment of her delighted squeals and squeaks, with a scrubbing brush. On alternate Sundays, she was anointed all over with expensive Neats Foot Oil and given a pedicure – after its teeth, an elephant's most vulnerable spot is its feet. My contribution to Tinker's renaissance was the eradication of the worms (at that time by giving a drench of piperazine salts) and injection of vitamins A and D followed by a prescription of daily quantities of vitamin C, calcium and iron.

Willie was a tall lanky youth with a long thin face topped by carrot red hair. His hands and feet were overlarge and he looked an awkward and ungainly fellow – until he moved among elephants. With them he was sure and deft and his voice with its deep broad Lancashire accent exerted a calming influence upon the mighty creatures. The elephants loved him and would caress him fondly with their trunk tips as he moved around them or slipped through their legs.

'There won't be no trouble will there, Doctor,' Willie asked me shortly after Tinker's arrival, 'with 'er getting over this anaemia like?' His long face looked troubled.

'Don't you worry Willie,' I replied, 'keep getting this diet into her and make sure she takes her vitamin C and iron tablets without fail.'

'The iron'll do 'er blood good, I suppose.'

'Yes. Twelve tablets crushed into the molasses mixture at her age. When she's bigger I'll probably increase the dose.'

Willie tended Tinker with utter devotion and took to sleeping in the elephant house at night on a pile of straw in the gallery above the animals, to be on hand if she got a spot of infant colic or even just felt peckish at any time. Not willing to trust anyone even Matt Kelly with looking after her while he was away, he elected to forego his days off.

'Ah wouldn't enjoy going to pub or t'pictures sitting there worrying how she were doing wi'out me, Doctor Taylor. It'd fair bother me,' he explained. Tinker had become Willie's life and with elephants being the most popular animal in any zoo and good elephant keepers being among the élite of zoo staff and very hard to come by, Willie looked forward, I think, to many happy years at Belle Vue. As he said, 'I reckon I'll be looking after this little lass till I retire!' It seemed probable at the time. Willie was then about 21 years of age.

All went well for the first four weeks after Tinker's arrival. Her condition improved dramatically, the mouth became pinker and the ankles firmer. Then one evening Matt Kelly rang and asked me to call in the following day to look at Tinker – something appeared to be wrong with her. Next morning I drove across to Manchester and was met by a distraught Willie and sombre Kelly standing outside the elephant house waiting for me.

'She's not eating this morning,' shouted the elephant keeper before I could get out of the car, 'and she's a bit funny on her legs!' I went in to look at the elephant. She stood quietly in her quarters staring at the wall. I gave her a gentle push and she did indeed stagger before regaining her balance. After making a full examination I was still puzzled.

No sign of the dreaded elephant colic or the always fatal twisted bowel. But she was panting slightly and her gums seemed more of an orange-pink than usual. No amount of pressing into her with a clenched fist evinced any evidence of pain. Boiled sweets, warm milk, swiss rolls – we tried all her favourite treats, but she would not so much as investigate them with her trunk. I took a blood sample from her ear and then gave her an injection of menbutone.

'Leave some glucose and water in front of her,' I said. 'I'll be back as soon as I get the analysis results.'

By late afternoon I had a list of numbers produced by the laboratory. Alongside the numbers were asterisks which signified that the laboratory machines, programmed to handle human blood and unfamiliar with elephant values, were drawing the physician's attention to the fact that this patient was *most* abnormal. In fact the numbers were within the normal ranges for the Asiatic elephant with certain exceptions – those relating to liver function. Tinker's liver was most definitely in trouble – but there was no hint as to the cause. Alarmed by the news – liver disease is very uncommon in young elephants – I drove back to Belle Vue to commence treatment to protect the liver cells by loading them with carbohydrates. I discussed the possible causes with Kelly after I had given Tinker some large shots of prednisolone and vitamin B12.

'No chance of her having eaten any ragwort plants is there?' I asked the Head Keeper. The city zoo did possess one field where weeds grew but Matt shook his head.

'She's never been out of the elephant house and we've cut no grass to bring in to her.'

I inspected the food and hay – they seemed free of suspect materials. There was no sign of bacterial activity in the blood samples and I wondered whether I should give antibiotics, nevertheless. Perhaps the damage was a delayed effect of all those worms which in their laval stage may have migrated through the liver tissues scarifying it. What else could damage the liver in this way? Copper poisoning could do it in some animals but we weren't giving any copper to Tinker. Sheep sometimes developed it when wrongly fed on diets designed for pigs that were supplemented with levels of copper too high for ovine species. Perhaps that could be it – I looked at the bags of concentrate food in the elephant house. None contained any copper. In desperation I reviewed with Matt and with Willie all the medicines, vitamins and minerals the little elephant had received. Nowhere was there any possibility, as far as I could see, of liver toxicity.

'Are you sure it's not that damned anaemia still?' asked Willie as I admitted defeat. 'My father keeps pigs on his smallholding. 'E were always losing 'em wi' anaemia. Bloody scores of 'em till vet put him on to iron injections.'

'No Willie, it's not anaemia,' I replied, 'the blood shows good numbers of red cells now and anyway you are still giving the iron pills.'

'I am indeed, Doc. She gets everything the best. You can rely on me.'

'By the way,' interrupted Matt, 'we could do with some more iron tablets when you're in next, David.'

'OK more iron tablets – hold on a minute Matt,' I replied, 'I brought another thousand in last week!' The Irishman scratched his head and reached for an almost empty bottle of red tablets standing on a shelf behind him.

'Willie here says he's almost out. Looks like it. Enough for a couple of days.'

'But there was a thousand in that last week!' I exclaimed. 'You can only have used eighty-four maximum by today!'

Matt turned to Willie. The elephant keeper's expression was one of frowning impassivity.

'Well, Willie – what have you done with them?' Kelly asked.

'Nowt,' the keeper said quietly after a pause. 'Just given 'em to Tinker, just to her.'

'But a thousand have gone!' I said. 'How many have you been giving her?'

Willie shuffled his big feet and picked at a bale of straw with sausage-like fingers.

'Come on?' bawled Matt suddenly. 'You heard what Doctor T said!'

Willie looked me straight in the eye. 'I haven't stolen 'em or eaten them Doctor Taylor – really. She's had 'em, Tinker. I've given 'em to 'er. For that anaemia.'

'How many Willie?' I asked.

'Ooh, about two handfuls a day I reckon,' he was clearly almost on the point of breaking into tears. 'You said it were anaemia and to give her twelve. But I thought a few extra would boost her up, make her right all the quicker.'

So that was it, instead of twelve the little elephant must have been receiving almost a hundred pills a day.

'Iron is poisonous in overdose, Willie,' I said quietly, 2,000 folk a year in the United States, mainly kids who think iron tablets are sweets, get iron poisoning and about 85 per cent of them die!'

'You bloody fool!' Matt's words were delivered slowly and with great venom.

'I only meant the best, you know that,' moaned Willie now mopping tears from his eyes with a piece of sacking. 'I didn't dream it'd harm her, Doctor Taylor!'

I felt deeply sorry for the lad. He'd harmed the one character that meant everything to him.

'I know that. Now enough of all this. We've got to try to pull Tinker round! No more iron tablets for the time being.'

'If she dies, you're fired Willie my lad!' grated Matt.

'If we're lucky, she won't!' I said. 'I'm going now to Manchester Royal. I'll try to get some chelating agent – a chemical that grabs excess iron in the body and renders it harmless.' I left the two of them standing there, Willie blubbering miserably and Matt glaring at the boy with one of his puce-coloured faces.

As luck would have it, I managed to obtain 100 vials of desferrioxamine from a concerned and highly co-operative pharmacist at the hospital a couple of miles away. We must have got it in the nick of time, for after a week of treatment Tinker began to make a steady recovery and eventually returned to the rudest of health, still tended by the luckless Willie.

'He's a good elephant man and I'm sure he's learnt his lesson,' I said to Matt when some weeks later we stood together watching Tinker having her toe-nails filed and polished with hoof oil. She was purring as Willie worked on her.

'Arrumph,' grunted the Head Keeper, 'I've docked three quid a week off his wages for a while. That'll teach him we've enough vets round here without him playing at doctors into the bargain!'

10 *The White Lady*

'My rattle snakes have lost their rattles. Please come and restore them.' Professor Lombardi, son of the famous Angelo Lombardi of Italy, the Roman Johnny Morris, is a noted zoologist in his own right. His request was the only one I have ever received from overseas expressly to visit snakes. Generally owners seem to consider it far cheaper to replace sick serpents than to stump up the cost of my air fare. Compared to most exotic mammals and birds, the majority of snakes cost peanuts. The Professor had several collections of venomous and non-venomous snakes in zoos and safari parks in the north of Italy and they included a number of rarer species. There are more than sixty-five kinds of rattle snake alone and one, found only on the tiny island of Bimini in the Bahamas, was the cause of Lombardi's concern – he possessed a precious trio of Bimini rattlers and for a week now they had looked decidedly uncomfortable and lacking, in so far as it is possible for snakes, in *joie de vivre*.

I have to work with the whole range of reptiles but I must admit that poisonous snakes do not turn me on. Quite simply, they frighten me. Cold in blood and in mind, inscrutable as stone, they are beyond reach of my empathy. I can't communicate linguistically with mammals or birds but I can so often *feel* with them, strike up some accord, no matter how transient. Snakes I can admire and wonder at as beautiful, talented and ingenious creatures but I cannot love them subjectively as I can tigers (deadly though they are), bears (treacherous as they can be) or ostriches (dimwitted as I suspect them to be). Their venom even when not fatal can cause horrifying and often permanent damage and a significant percentage of the most experienced collectors and handlers of dangerous snakes have in the past been killed by their quarry. Nevertheless, I agreed to go to Piedmont to advise upon the out-of-sorts ophidians. The visit turned out to be even more than I had bargained for – though the rattle snakes on this occasion proved as little trouble as a clowder of cuddly kittens.

The problem turned out to be infestation of the snakes' lungs by a most odd-looking but common parasite. Looking like a long yellow caterpillar, the parasite, a pentastome, is actually a sort of mite deformed and adapted to life inside the reptile over millions of years of evolution. It can be killed by hanging up organophosphorus insecticidal strips in the terarium for measured periods and this is what I told Lombardi to do. After inspecting all the Professor's snakes and discussing general health measures, he asked me if I would care to visit a friend of his while I was in the country.

'The Conte di Mercati is a great lover of animals. I told him you were coming, Doctor, and he is most anxious for you to see some of his reptiles.'

'Has he also got problems?' I asked.

'Yes, he needs your help. He is a very rich man, a distinguished patron of the arts and a devotee, you can say, like me of the snake goddess. Please go to Ivrea, Count Mercati is a man you should know.'

It would add another day to the trip but Ivrea was only 100 miles away. 'OK,' I said, 'but did he say what the trouble was? What animal?'

'He did not,' replied Lombardi, 'but go, go my friend you will like Mercati – and he speaks excellent English.' I travelled by very slow train to Ivrea. It took half a day and there was no seat to be found so I sat on The Bag in a crowded corridor within a thicket of legs of soldiers and plump country women and surrounded by an undergrowth of pungent tobacco ash, wine bottles and some live chickens. I arrived in a bad humour but Lombardi had 'phoned to advise the Count of my coming and my mood was uplifted when I alighted from the train to be greeted by two men in dark green uniforms, one of whom carried one of those boards with a little bell on top that are used to locate guests in good hotels. The board had 'Dr Tailor' chalked upon it. They introduced themselves as servants of Il Conte and led me to a most imposing two-horse open carriage waiting outside the station. In solitary splendour I sat in the back while the men in green rode up front, backs like vertical ramrods. We clip-clopped at a cracking pace along gravelly tracks lined by tall cypresses. The autumn sun was setting, a copper disc slowly rolling along behind the hazy hills. I could smell wood smoke, hay, horse and the evening damp rising from the fields. It might have been Gloucestershire except for the red tiled roofs of the stone farmhouses and the occasional flooded rice field. After a fifteen-minute drive we swung in through two tall gateposts surmounted by marble lions rampant. A flagstone driveway led us, wheels ringing, through dense, square-cut box-tree hedges as tall as a house to end abruptly after some one hundred metres in front of a small renaissance villa. Its flaky pale grey façade peeped out from behind a green veil of creepers. A staircase and terrace of soft pink marble had white and pink flowering weeds jostling in every crack and cranny between the stonework and led up to the main door of elaborately chased copper on wood. An ancient patina of verdigris made the door a pale and luminescent aquamarine in the fading light. The carriage came to a halt and I helped The Bag down. At once a butler in black suit and white gloves came hurrying out of the big green door and, after bowing politely and waving the carriage away, led the way up the staircase and into the house.

The lofty hall that I entered was floored and lined with green veined white marble. It was crowded with beautiful things – rich paintings, gilded wood and satin furniture, statuettes of bronze, pewter and alabaster, tall palms in large amphorae and a dozen glittering and ticking clocks. A tall stooped man came towards me hand outstretched. He was silver haired and had pale and aquiline features though the dark and shining eyes projected a humane warmth. He was about 70 years of age I reckoned and walked with the aid of a gold topped ebony cane.

'Doctor Taylor!' said Mercati. His voice was faint and hoarse but his English was flawless. 'How very kind of you to come, welcome to the Villa Martin. The villa of the kingfisher. An appropriate name – there are so many of those beautiful birds along the stream in the gardens here. Alberto!' He looked over my shoulder to the butler, 'Take the Doctor's bag to the Giotto. Come,' he said to me, 'you have had a tiring journey from Pombia, I am sure you will appreciate some tea.'

He led me into a small windowless library where walls of books from floor to ceiling surrounded chairs and a table of crimson leather. A fire danced in the grate borne on the back of the ornate bronze turtle that inhabited the marble fireplace. An exquisite Royal Worcester tea-set was laid on the table. Mercati poured the tea and we settled into the deep chairs.

'The tea is my personal blend. I hope you like it,' said my host. 'I still have it sent from the same shop in Cambridge that made it up for me when I was at King's reading English Literature.'

It was magnificent tea – the water of North Italy beats the hard stuff with which the Thames Water Authority consistently manages to prevent me making an even passable brew in Lightwater. 'Professor Lombardi was not able to tell me anything about the animal trouble you have,' I said, 'what . . .'

Mercati wagged a long pale finger and gave a charming smile.

'Doctor, it is too late today. You are my guest tonight. We can see her tomorrow morning. You will fly from Torino, no? In the afternoon?'

'And *she* is what?'

'She is the White Lady!' Mercati looked at me with his dark eyes twinkling over his teacup. 'A very special lady – you will like her.'

'Lombardi said you were a reptile enthusiast,' I was fishing for a clue. The obviously cultured old fellow didn't look like the alligator-in-the-bath type. No, perhaps in the gardens there would be Roman fountains and a thermal spring that supplied a poolful of European turtles. That seemed more in keeping. But White Lady? Mercati chose not to enlighten me further.

'You're arrival tonight is a most fortunate chance. I am an inveterate Anglophile, as you may imagine, and have many English friends living nearby. Are you a literary man, Doctor?'

'Well, I love books but . . .'

'What about the Owl and the Pussy Cat?'

I was beginning to wonder whether he wasn't after all the alligator-in-the-bath sort. 'Oh, Edward Lear – putting to sea . . .'

'Yes – do you love Lear?'

'Some, most of his poems – but I find his limericks rather weak.' The thought came to me that I might be expected to spend an evening discussing English literature with a pleasant eccentric.

'Quite agree. But you see there's a Jabberwock party at the Villa Pioppo, the home of my good friends the Hursts, tonight. English people. He was in the embassy at Rome till he retired. Great fun. And they'd love you to come along.'

'Ah but . . . that's most kind. But I'm not dressed for socialising and I'm only carrying a change of shirt. I didn't expect when I went to Lombardi's . . .' I would dearly have preferred to see the White Lady whatever she was, get her dealt with, go to bed and then be off early in the morning. Mercati gave a hoarse but merry laugh.

'Dress – that's no trouble at all. You see we are all dressing for dinner.' He laughed again and poured more tea. 'Not black tie or anything like that. Mary Hurst has decreed it shall be an Edward Lear party. Everyone's going in costume.'

'But Count Mercati,' Why do I keep finding myself in situations which are farther and farther removed from the profession of veterinary medicine and often do seem pure Lear? 'I would prefer to stay here and look at your animals. A fancy dress party is . . .'

'*Sciocchezze*!' It was the first word of Italian my host had used to me. 'No trouble at all. Alberto can fit you up with the necessary. Didn't have enough notice to find the appurtenances of a walrus (he gestured towards my moustache) but we'll turn you into a most satisfactory carpenter.' I couldn't believe my ears. 'I,' continued the Count, 'am going with this!' He rose and went over to the mantelpiece and returned with a plate that I had not noticed up to that moment. On the plate was a round pie with a Purple Emperor butterfly pinned to its crust. 'I shall be the White Knight!' God, if only I could remember all the poems, I thought. White Ladies, White Knights, walruses and carpenters! Ah yes, that was it. 'I look for butterflies that sleep among the wheat, I make them into mutton pies and sell them in the street.' Definitely I had landed in oddball country. Alligators in the bath were now odds-on favourite. An hour later feeling utterly ridiculous and something of a hybrid between characters out of Lear and Lewis Carroll, I sat once more in the carriage next to a cheerful Italian nobleman dressed in a white patchwork suit and carrying the pie on his lap. Alberto the butler had provided me with a leather apron and a long woodsaw. I was now indubitably The Carpenter. With paraffin coach lights flickering in the gloom of the Italian countryside, we rattled off to dinner. Although it was dark and buried in a wood of plain trees, my impression of the villa at which we shortly arrived was that it was much larger than Mercati's. Resignedly I followed the White Knight up the steps to the open door that blazed light. We were greeted by an Oyster – the lady of the house, a rotund character in a tight fitting, silver-grey gown with an opalescent oval of some material glued to her backside.

'Da - - - - arlings!' she brayed and kissed me with the continental quadruple that now seems to be in fashion, as if we'd met only last week either at Baden-Baden or the Royal Enclosure. 'You're the fourth carpenter we've got and there's a positive plethora of Jabberwockies.' Thrusting a glass of something purple into my hand she sailed away. We were in a hall again – not dissimilar to that of the other villa and full of chattering people in extraordinary garb. There were obvious Dongs – they were the people with fluorescent paint on their noses – and plenty of Ploffskins, Pluffskins and Pelican jees in mock pelican costume. I couldn't place a near naked girl in gold varnish and scrap of net – a Jumbly-girl? But she should have had sky blue hands and sea green hair. An already inebriate Italian gentleman, in a tattered frock coat and long false beard that reached down to his knees, slumped in a chair and sipping the purple stuff (a Parfait Amour cocktail I discovered later) had a label pinned to one lapel inscribed 'Father William'. Mercati disappeared deep in Italian conversation with another White Knight. Our hostess came back carrying a gilded plastic ring.

'Look what Freddie Barber, the piggy over there gave me – now do tell me, sorry, – I'm terrible at remembering names – what has Ludo Mercati been telling you about me?' She offered me a tray of small mince and quince tartlets but with a glass in one hand and my saw in the other I was stymied.

'Oh, nothing actually,' I replied.

'*Really*! how banal of the sweet man. Are you out here from Sothebys then?'

'Sothebys – oh no. I'm a veterinary surgeon.' The Oyster gave me a big wink.

'Sotheby's valuers always say that when they're out here doing appraisals.'

I winked back enigmatically and began to feel panicky. Suppose Hanne had got some urgent messages for me.

'Do tell me, is Ludo really going to sell that little Caravaggio?' The purple stuff had got into my system.

'Not now he knows its provenance is suspect,' I replied leaning close to her left ear. The Oyster's eyes widened fit to fall out like those of a Père David deer I once had trouble with.

'Reeeeelly. Now that is juicy!'

'Tell me Mrs Hurst – confidentially,' I got as close as I could without damaging her shell, 'Count Mercati's White Lady – what is it exactly?'

She pulled back from me, looked at me blankly for a moment and then giggled. 'Oh Doctor – the White Lady now, she's really something – you *must* have seen her.'

An Owl grabbed her by the arm and dragged her away before she could finish answering me.

'Are you Pinky's old man? The one with that ginormous yacht at Sorrento?' purred another younger and more curvy little Oyster who drifted over and began behaving as if there really were an R in the month.

'Er no, I'm – I'm the White Lady's doctor,' I countered hoping she was a friend or acquaintance of Mercatis. She wobbled my saw Rolf Harris style.

'White Lady?' she said. 'Wrong author sweetie, White Knight OK, White Lady zerisimo. There just is no such lady in Lear. Anyway you look more like a carpenter to me, how about you and me taking a little walk?'

I was saved by the arrival upon the scene of a jolly Dong with a red ping pong ball glued to his nose who announced that he was her boyfriend. I have never been more relieved to get away from a party. Mercati mercifully suggested we leave at midnight and he recited Edward Lear verses word perfect in his hoarse voice during the drive back.

I slept in a four-poster bed in an exquisite room full of small paintings by the fourteenth-century painter Giotto and woke in the morning to the sound of Vivaldi's music filling the villa. It was raining heavily and I had a legacy of the purple cocktail in the form of a throbbing head. An aspirin, a quick cup of coffee and I must see this White Lady thing without delay, do what I can and be on my way to Turin, I thought, as I dressed. I wouldn't be surprised if Mercati hasn't got some of his expatriate literati coming around for a G. K. Chesterton brunch or something and then I'd perhaps be inveigled into staying over as Father Brown! No thank you. The butler served me the coffee in a dining room that looked out through high windows on to a small lake surrounded by poplars. Mercati came in, limping slightly on his cane and shook me by the hand.

'Good morning, Doctor. No breakfast? Well, I suppose it's time to go and see the White Lady. I hope she's in a sweet temper on such a filthy morning!' He smiled mischievously and beckoned me to follow him. 'Come along, let's go and pay our respects.'

We left the villa proper to walk along a covered walk of white marble that crossed a garden of low bushes to a round and green domed pavilion. This was also built of marble and was encircled by a number of tall windows. Mercati opened a door and ushered me into the pavilion. I was met by a gush of warm moist air and found myself immediately in a tropical rain forest. Palms, lianas, bamboo and orchids grew in profusion. There were mossy banks and giant ferns, dripping pools and invisible birds that chirped high in the foliage. A gravel path wound through the vegetation. Spotlights threw circles of light in the dark green gloom and illuminated glass-fronted vivaria set at intervals along the sides of the path. In these cases were reptiles of many kinds, mainly fine specimens of rare species and some that are seldom seen in zoos. There were chameleons, a pair of deadly taipans from Australia and incredibly a tuatara! – the very rare and protected New Zealand lizard that possesses the remains of a mysterious third eye in its head and whose eggs take a year to hatch! I nearly choked on my words.

'A tuatara! . . . how? . . . the New Zealand Government . . . where did you?'

Mercati raised a white finger to thinly smiling lips but kept his eyes fixed avidly on the reptile which was crouched motionless on a moss-coloured log. 'Would you believe, Doctor, nothing in this world cannot be obtained – if one has the wherewithal. In Orlando's case here – an early Modigliani.' He lifted the lid of the tuatara's vivarium and dropped in a locust that he produced from somewhere.

'You exchanged it for a picture?' I croaked, as the lizard munched the insect. Mercati nodded.

'Let us say the picture was taken in exchange for exit visas for Orlando and his mate – she's in there somewhere.'

I frequently hear rumours of wealthy animal fanciers obtaining rare and endangered species for private collections by either arranging for their theft or alternatively bribing government officials in charge of licensing and conservation of the creatures. Unimpeded passage through the borders of most countries could be similarly arranged and anyway what customs man could tell that Orlando was not a common green iguana or pick out a very rare kind of tortoise from a commonplace one or an endangered tropical bird from one that was just as colourful but not under protection. (At least British Customs officials, while by no means consistently efficient, can and often do call on expert zoological back-up to identify shipments of exotic livestock.)

'I suppose you could get a Komodo Dragon if you cared to,' I murmured half-heartedly. It was wonderful to see the tuatara but the means of its acquisition, as ever on such occasions, disgusted me.

'Oh, no trouble at all my dear friend,' replied Mercati, 'you know Indonesia. The place teems with officials with ever itchy palms. Perhaps one day when I construct a big enough installation for them . . .'

He moved on and I followed him round a sharp bend in the path.

Before us and almost surrounded by tall green reeds was a cylindrical object about 4 feet in diameter and 6 feet high. It was enveloped in dark green velvet material. Mercati came to a halt. In a hoarse whisper he said, 'Now. You will see her. The White Lady. Prepare to do obeisance.' He gave a low chuckle. I admit that by now after the previous evening's fantasies and this morning's unexpected encounter with a real live tuatara, I was distinctly and deliciously excited at the prospect of at last coming face to face with her ladyship. If she turned out to be a pigmy Tyrannosaurus rex, I would not have been surprised. Mercati seemed capable of anything. My host walked up to the green draped object and pulled at the velvet cover. It fell away to reveal an all glass cylinder with a wire mesh lid fastened by brass clasps and a floor carpeted in dry leaves.

The White Lady was revealed, staring at us unblinking, for her sort cannot blink. She was white of skin and had rich ruby eyes. *Ophiophagus hannah*! And an albino at that! Lying coil upon coil in the centre of the cylinder was an unpigmented king cobra, the biggest venomous snake I had ever seen – about 16 feet long, as far as I could reckon.

'Well, Doctor,' said Mercati proudly after he'd given me time to take in the sheer magnificence of the animal, 'what do you say?'

'I say it is a most incredible beast', I replied, 'where did you obtain it?' King cobras or Hamadryads, the largest of all venomous snakes and the most aggressive, are usually yellowish green with dark bands and come from the deep jungles of Burma, Malaya, Vietnam, the Philippiness and South China. Many snake experts rate them as the most dangerous serpents in the world.

'It came to me via a dealer in Thailand,' said the Count. 'As an albino it cost me about one hundred times the normal price!' It wasn't the first albino cobra I had met – there had been another one, owned by Drayton Manor Zoo which I presented as an item on 'Animal Magic' for the BBC. But this one was twice the size of the other!

'And it wasn't just the albinism that boosted its value,' continued Mercati. 'According to the old thief who sold it, it had been cut from the belly of a Thai woman who'd swallowed it accidentally as an egg. It hatched and grew in her stomach and had to be cut out by a surgeon.'

'Do you believe that?' I asked.

'Who knows? I think not, however. But I was shown a young *ragazza* in Bangkok with a scar on her abdomen who everyone said was the patient in question!'

Stories of live snakes being vomited or passed in the faeces of human beings are not uncommon in the writings of ancient medical men. Hippocrates talks about it and Donatus, a sixteenth-century writer, records the case of a viper which had previously crawled into the mouth emerging eventually from the anus. It is difficult to know what to make of bizarre accounts such as these. The most recent and fascinating such incident is recounted in a UPI press report from Damascus in March 1982. The Syrian daily *Al Baath* reported that 'a young woman who underwent surgery for severe stomach pains had a six foot snake in her intestines. Surgeons were unable to remove the snake because it had hatched inside her stomach, curling around the intestines as it grew'. Doctors reportedly speculated that the woman, 25-year-old Khadija El Reefi, from the town of Aleppo, drank well water polluted with snake eggs as a child. Initial surgery in Syria to remove the snake was unsuccessful and Khadija was sent to Spain for a second operation. It did not name the city or the hospital but said doctors again failed to remove the snake – despite using anaesthesia on it. Witnesses said 'the snake cheeped like a chicken when it was hungry and it was plain that Khadija and people near her could hear the snake sounds'. I tried to check up upon this story in Spain but to no avail. I find it difficult to believe that the luckless Khadija really had a snake inside her but, nevertheless, I wished they'd sent for me when they were trying to 'anaesthetise' it – if it really was a snake, a shot of one of our special reptile anaesthetics would quickly have relaxed it so that it could have been disentangled from whatever it was wound around in the poor woman's insides. Tales such as this, I assume, must be magnified distortions of incidents involving abdominal tumours of unusual shape or parasitism by large species of round worm or tape worms. That, of course, does not explain the 'cheeping' sounds emanating from Khadija's stomach. Unless it was rather high pitched wind!

The White Lady raised her head and expanded some of her ribs to display the sinister hood as I walked up to her glass palace. She obviously didn't like what she saw. There was more of a harsh roar than a hiss as she exhaled an angry breath. Her jaws were as big as my clenched fist – behind the thin white lips I glimpsed pink gum and the ridge shielding short fangs, which could inject enough poison at any one time to kill perhaps fifteen people.

'She is always a bit like that before I feed her,' whispered Mercati. 'Wait – I will give her a titbit.' He opened a box lying in the reeds and took out a wriggling grass snake. King cobras feed normally on live snakes and the provision of such a diet is one of the difficulties of keeping them in captivity. The White Lady kept her eyes fixedly on me as he reached up, opened the lid of the cylinder and dropped in the living 'titbit'. It fell near the cobra and began to slide away beneath the brown and golden leaves. Imperiously the White Lady turned her gaze away from me and regarded the titbit, by now half disappeared. A flash of white like the silent crack of a whip and she struck. Her jaws sank into the grass snake halfway along its body length impaling it deeply on the fangs. The victim writhed as its massive assailant held on, chewing again and again in classic cobra fashion to inject more and more venom. Blood ran from the cobra's mouth as her powerful nerve poison began to take its effect on the prey. The grass snake quickly weakened and after a few minutes lay limp within her maw. When she could no longer detect any movement, the White Lady ceased the vicious chewing and began to draw the U-shaped body into her mouth by steady movement of flexible jaws and backward pointing teeth.

'Now is the time for you to examine her, Doctor,' said Mercati, 'while she's occupied with swallowing.'

'But . . .' I felt suddenly cold down the length of my spinal cord as I looked at the great snake.

'Count Mercati – what is it that concerns you about the . . . the White Lady?' The Italian tapped gently on the glass with his walking stick but the snake swallowed on impassively.

'Lumps under the skin along her body. There are five or six of them as big as cherries. Can't see them when she's coiled like this. You'll have to get her out for a close inspection.'

Get her out. Sixteen feet of muscle like animated steel cable, a temper that is vitriolic at the best of times, quick reactions (not quite as fast as a human being who's paying attention but fatally fast enough) and a bite that pumps in large quantities of very poisonous venom. Get her out! I was frightened. I frequently am – very – when working with venomous snakes. Once I used to deny it even to myself; there was no bravado, just my feeling that it was unprofessional to be afraid. I eventually learned sense, particularly after one of the reptile keepers at Belle Vue, a man of great experience and wisdom in the ways of snakes, was bitten by a Gaboon viper. I saw the deep wounds on the man's hand made by this often docile animal, which had the longest fangs of all snakes, and watched the terrible haemorrhage and swelling in the fingers develop and the near fatal collapse of his circulation that was reversed in the nick of time by the anti-venin which we rushed with him to the hospital. The poor fellow had agonising cramps, passed bloody urine for a week and lost three fingers – many of his worst symptoms being due to the side-effects of the viper anti-venin. But he eventually recovered. And it had all happened because we were force-feeding the snake which had gone into the sort of anorexia nervosa to which such creatures are prone. While opening the viper's jaws for me to introduce a dead white mouse that had been heavily injected with nicotinic acid and lubricated with lard, he had been, as he put it a moment later when he stared in horror at the two red-welling puncture marks on his palm, 'a bit butter fingered' in allowing his grip on the snake's head to slacken. The Gaboon viper, a species that doesn't go looking for trouble like, say, a cobra or a Javan krait, but insensed at having its fast so rudely interrupted, had struck perhaps more in sorrow than in anger.

I developed a greater respect for a snake's lethal abilities after that and lost my fear of feeling fear of them. At times, I argued it wasn't worth the risk to life or limb getting to grips with creatures which were of little monetary value and generally easily replaced. The actuarial statistics, the betting odds were all wrong when it came to snakes. One slip with a cockatoo or even an elephant wasn't likely to be as damaging as a miscalculation with this most ancient of man's enemies. There are 20,000 snake bite deaths a year in India alone. Snakes kill more people per year than sharks do in a century, more people in a month than big cats do in a century and more people in a day than rogue elephants have since time began. One prick of a fang that happens to enter a superficial vein and even the existence of appropriate antidote serum closeby will not save you. So it was easier to avoid the dangerously venomous species or to guess-diagnose them without handling them from the other side of the glass. But the less I handled the snakes, the less sure my hand movements became when I *had* to touch them. And that increased the likelihood of a fumble and a consequent bite. My fear might mean more care and more respect, but it might also mean more trembling hands – more 'butter fingers'. And there were so many things that had to be done by the fingers that couldn't be done at a distance with the aid of long tongs or snake grabber devices. It was difficult to know what line to take on the killer snake.

Faced with the prospect of arm wrestling the White Lady I at once made up my mind that discretion should remain the better part of valour. Life was worth more than any albino king cobra – no matter how aristocratic. I had a feeling that the White Lady would be coldly unforgiving of a fumble. No *noblesse oblige* there.

'I'll gladly examine her,' I said, 'but someone will have to catch her and hold her securely.' Mercati nodded with a smile. I detected a trace of mocking in his pale face and glittering eyes.

'You are right, Doctor – I will seize her!'

'Are you sure? Have you handled her before?' This was an even more worrying turn of events. The limping old man was a whiz with Victorian comic verse but how good was he at safely nabbing and then keeping a firm grip upon a powerful and malevolent reptile weighing 40 pounds or more. I needed to know that before I went any further. An unreliable assistant is more dangerous than one's own unreliable hands. In the latter case, at least you've only got yourself to look out for.

'My dear boy,' Mercati purred, 'I have been handling beasts such as m'lady here since I was a young man. You can rest assured that you and she will be in safe hands.'

He pointed to a sliding curved panel of glass at the bottom of the cylinder.

'I shall bring her out through there when you are ready.'

I took The Bag off my shoulder, unzipped it and put it down on the pathway. In the side pocket within easy reach was a vial of polyvalent Far Eastern elapid anti-venin, in other words, a serum obtained from the Pasteur Institute in

France against the poison of various members of the cobra family, including the King. Strapped to it was a ready-to-use sterilised syringe and needle.

'Please go ahead,' I said, 'I'm ready whenever you are.'

I'd made a mental note of a spade leaning against a palm tree to my right and within arm's length. The words of Matt Kelly came back to me. As a young student he'd told me that 'the best emergency weapon in a toyt corner is a spade. If you're really up against it m'lad, one good swoipe can break a tiger's back or behead a rattler!' It had sounded gruesome enough at the time but the proximity of the spade in Mercati's tropical house did make me feel, if not armed, at least a little comforted. I prayed that I would not need to put my Irish mentor's axiom to the test.

The White Lady was still ingesting the grass snake as Mercati bent down and slipped open the glass panel. I held my breath and watched him cautiously poke his walking stick, gold topped handle first, into the cylinder. The handle was an asymmetrical T-shape and he brought it towards the snake held down close to the leaves. His dark eyes were set intently on the serpent and his expression was one of frowning concentration.

'*Cosi*!' he cried, suddenly bringing the handle down on the back of the White Lady's neck just below the hood which at once flared to its full expanse. He pressed the snake's head down hard and her long white body began to uncoil and thrash sending up a shower of dried leaves. That roar again! Mercati swiftly moved his other arm through the opening as soon as the snake was firmly pinned by the stick and grasped it tightly around the jaws. Bang – the cobra's tail slammed violently against the glass. Now dropping the stick the Italian used his free hand to take a second hold on the cobra about two feet behind its head. His fingers only managed to half encircle the animal's girth at this point. With a grunt of triumph he straightened up and withdrew the snake, the bulk of its body lashing impotently from side to side. There was the acrid smell of snake droppings, voided at the moment of combat, in the air. The White Lady was a fearsomely impressive beast, the head and tail tip of the grass snake still protruding from her half-gaping mouth. Her blood-flecked lips matched the ruby of her eyes and together with her deathly pallor and unremittingly icy gaze, added to an appearance of pure evil. Of course, there is no such thing as an evil animal but as I looked at the huge cobra I sensed not fear or desperation in her, but a distinct, disturbing and consuming hatred. A dew of cold sweat condensed upon my forehead. If Mercati's grip relaxed now, if he got cramp in his fingers, the White Lady, no thought of simply scuttling for safety, would wreak a terrible vengeance upon us. At least, I thought, death from cobra venom is preferable to that induced by a rattlesnake or a pit viper such as the Fer-de-lance. Being a nerve as opposed to a blood poison, the venom causes first drooping eyelids, then sleepiness and finally paralysis. No pain except for the bite wound itself. Some of the great venomous snake experts of the past who were at last caught out by one of their animals, coolly wrote about their symptoms during their final hours. In the case of cobras it didn't sound too bad.

No time to waste now in examining my patient. 'Are you happy with your hold?' I asked Mercati.

'Yes. No trouble. I have her,' he replied.

I ran my hands down the length of the White Lady's body. There is a pleasing smooth dry feel to snakes, not at all the cold slimy quality many people imagine. She was in magnificent condition. Firm, shiny and well nourished. No sign of the tiny parasitic mites that one often finds managing to scrounge shelter and sustenance under the free edge of snake skin scales. But there were, as Mercati had described, half a dozen round hard lumps beneath the skin scattered at irregular intervals. I probed the lumps with the tips of my fingers. They moved slightly feeling like marbles that had somehow been implanted there.

'What do you think, Doctor? Tumour?'

I shook my head. I had come across many such cases before in a wide variety of snake species.

'No,' I said, 'not tumours – these are cold abscesses, generally filled with hard rubbery pus. They may be the serpent equivalent of human acne, but I suspect they develop around a nucleus formed by a long dead parasite such as a tapeworm cyst. They tend to grow slowly. The best thing is to cut them out.'

Mercati sucked in his breath sharply.

'Operate on the White Lady, Doctor? Do you think you can quieten, anaesthetise her, safely?' I took him to be referring to the snake's safety not ours.

'I never use general anaesthetic for removal of these things,' I said, 'they are best dealt with by freezing.' The Count looked relieved and kissed his deadly lady on the tip of her nose within a whisker of the visible portions of grass snake.

'Careful, Count!' I said, 'if there's any venom lying around her mouth it can be dangerous if you inadvertently swallow any.'

'I thought venom was harmless if swallowed.'

'There are suspicions that *cobra* venom can act orally and certainly any venom may get into the blood if you have an abrasion in the mouth or even an ulcer in the stomach!' I went to The Bag for the necessary equipment – an ethyl chloride freezing bottle, a scalpel, some cotton wool and a little bottle of iodine.

'Grip still OK?' I asked.

'Yes, yes.' The cobra still thrashed three-quarters of its length. I swabbed the first lump with iodine and then directed a jet of ethyl chloride at it from a distance of a few inches. Allowing a couple of seconds for the liquid to evaporate and chill the part, I then slit the skin over the swelling with one stab of the scalpel. Pressing with my fingers I then popped out a smooth yellow green mass, looking rather like an olive and leaving a clean cavity behind. I dipped a twist of cotton wool into the iodine and then held it in the hole for a moment before withdrawing it. Done. Important not to suture up. The hole would heal without any further attention within a couple of weeks or so. I moved on to treat the next lump in like manner.

I was about to express the core of the fifth abscess when, at that moment, Mercati said quietly, 'Doctor – I'm in trouble!' I looked up at him and was again conscious of the sweat now forming into rivulets that ran stinging into my eyes. The Count was looking at the cobra's head. Her jaws were askew. She was chomping them again. As she swung her body about, Mercati's grip on the smooth head was being progressively altered. His fingers I saw were much closer to her teeth than before – slowly and steadily the White Lady was loosening herself from his grasp.

'Can you take a better hold?' I asked. 'I'll grab her neck if you wish while . . . '

'No. Too dangerous!' he replied grimly. 'Changing hands or even opening this hand to move it back will give her the split second she needs . . . '

'Well, what . . .?' I felt sick. He couldn't alter his grip for fear of her striking. And if he did nothing she'd be free anyway before long. Either way there was going to be a king cobra running amok.

'I can feel her head slipping through my palm,' Mercati murmured calmly. I glanced quickly to check on the spade.

'I'm going to lose her Doctor! There's just one chance!'

He was speaking as quietly and precisely as if he were merely enquiring the price of a secondhand copy of poetry in some antiquarian bookshop. 'When I feel she's about to go, I'll fling her from me as far as possible over there,' he nodded towards a banana bush heavy with fruit. 'Hopefully I'll stun rather than kill her. Then you make for the door as fast as you can Doctor. I'll be OK with the stick if you'll be so good as to pick it up and stick it into the earth close by me. Now –

get on with the cutting! I'll give you the word when we arrive at the moment of truth!'

I picked up Mercati's stick and placed it where he'd indicated and then went back to working on the abscess. I felt light headed now, dry in the mouth and most decidedly uninterested in chronic cobra abscess surgery. The blood surged noisily in my ears as I cleaned out the cavity and reached for the ethyl chloride for the final lump. The briefest of sprays and I stabbed in the sharp blade. A squeeze and then another blood-tinged lump fell to the ground. Just half a minute more, I thought frantically shaking iodine on to cotton wool and . . .

'GO!!' yelled Mercati all at once. He staggered and almost fell as he brought the snake up above his head and then hurled it with a great gasp at the effort towards the banana bush. It hit the base of the trunk in a flurry of white, fell to the mossy undergrowth and to my horror instantly sorted itself out with no signs of being stunned or even dazed.

'Go!' shouted Mercati again, his voice hoarse and urgent. I now had the spade in my hand and was holding it like a cricket bat in the orthodox position for receiving fast bowled cobras – the blade protecting my legs. Beneath the banana leaves the White Lady reared a whole two feet from the ground and began to flow silently, hood displayed, towards us. A snake's method of forward movement, using a wave of muscular contractions which pass down the body from front to back, gives an impression of great speed but the truth is that except for short bursts the maximum speed they are capable of is about six or seven miles per hour. As the cobra advanced at what seemed like ten times that velocity, I froze. Mercati flicked out with his stick and caught her below the hood. With a vicious hiss, she struck at the ferrule and I saw some drops of cloudy yellow liquid fall to the ground. Deflected by the stick the white snake turned to face me more squarely and drew back its head while keeping its red eyes clamped firmly on me. A surge of adrenalin mercifully unlocked my limbs and I pushed the spade out in front of me. Clang! The White Lady struck again, recoiled and then tried to outflank the metal blade to strike my right leg from the side. Mercati lunged again with his stick but she flowed over it ignoring him and concentrating on me.

'You will have to kill her, Doctor. Use the spade!' cried my companion. 'Mother of God, go for her head!' My panic had suddenly crystallised and I entered the ice cold realm where thinking is again measured and deliberate and which always comes over me when, say, a major artery ruptures or a heart begins to fibrillate while I'm operating. It's the quiet eye in the hurricane. Although it was all happening in microseconds, my mind seemed to have all the time in the world to analyse the position. If I lifted the spade and drew it back to take a side swipe at the snake's erect head, it would leave my legs exposed to her fangs. The idea of killing the White Lady, decapitating her was, however, abhorrent. No. I would try pushing the spade out to her again and then move my body to one side. If she would stay involved with the implement, perhaps I might get into a position where I could approach her from her flank. I proffered the spade holding it in both hands. She struck hard breaking the tips off both fangs and I arched my body away from her and shuffled round to the left. She prepared to do battle again with the spade as I took up my new position. With a quick twist of the wrist and a metallic ring I swung the spade over and brought it down so that the flat of the blade swept her head and neck to the ground. She lay on damp earth just beside the pathway, her body writhing furiously once more. If the soil gave way she might be able to withdraw her head and start hostilities all over again, so I put a foot on the spade and stood on it with all my weight. Mercati limped over as fast as he could and bent down to seize her once more.

'Thank you, thank you – it would have been a tragedy to have had to kill her,' he said, purring again as I removed the spade. 'Now, do you wish to finish the last cavity?'

Noticeably weak at the knees and drenched in sweat, I completed the dressing of the final wound and then sat wearily on a rock to watch as Mercati threw the cobra back into her glass cylinder. He closed the sliding panel over the aperture just as she struck at it.

'That was a close call!' I said, as we walked back towards the villa. 'Don't you ever use snake tongs?' The Italian laughed gently.

'Why should I use snake tongs when I've got my stick?'

'She'll get you one day, Count.'

'The White Lady? No, I think not. I hope never to have to come to grips with her like that again.'

'How many times have you handled her before?'

'Oh, Doctor. This was the first time and I've had her seventeen years! Now – what about a Cappuccino and a generous dose of grappa?'

The White Lady's incisions healed up without complications and to date, touch wood, she has not been in need of any further ministrations from me. By a long chalk I consider her the most dangerous animal I've ever been called upon to deal with. As I said to Count Mercati later in the morning, when he bade me farewell and I climbed into the carriage that was to take me back to the railway station, 'Give me a big, bad, brutal Jabberwocky for a patient any day!'

11 *A Bit Tame, A Bit Wild*

There are times when one must most definitely not call a tiger a tiger. This was one of them. My companion, Karim, was a small wiry Bengali with oily black hair above a flattened round face that reminded me rather of a Pekinese. He wore nothing but a pair of baggy red-checked shorts as he sat behind me in the open black boat, in charge of the temperamental and seemingly bronchitic outboard motor that was hard pressed to make headway against the strong tide coming upstream.

'We are entering the forest now,' he whispered, 'please remember that once inside it is very bad luck, very dangerous to mention the . . . great cat by name. He will hear and be angry. Men die each year because they ignore this rule.'

'OK,' I replied. 'I will not say his name.'

'If you wish to speak of him it is permissible to say Mamaa – uncle or Bara miah – Great Lord. You understand?'

'I understand.'

It was March 1970 and I was passing through India on my way back to Europe after visiting Asia in search of dolphins and sea cows on behalf of Pentland Hick, the owner of Flamingo Park Zoo in Yorkshire. In Calcutta, I had visited the zoo and while there had been approached by one of the veterinarians with a most intriguing story. Essentially it was that there were reports from the Bay of Bengal, in the region of the Ganges river delta, of a mysterious and deadly epidemic among the local otters particularly those used by fishermen there – for fishing! Had I any idea as to what might be the nature of such an outbreak? I could think of several possibilities but without more information it was impossible to pass an opinion. But I leapt at the chance to find out. Would it be possible, I asked, for me to go and see some of the afflicted otters? There was no question of fees. No trouble at all, was the answer – if I could pay my way down into the delta. There were no vets in the area, no facilities, no accommodation and no transport unless I could hire a boat. Just lots of water and measureless miles of mangrove forest. Pentland Hick typically gave the go ahead when I cabled him. 'And keep an eye open for dugongs,' he added in a postscript.

The mangrove forests of the Sundarbans lie on the coast and straddle the border between Indian West Bengal and what was then Pakistani East Bengal, now Bangladesh. Here the great plain of the Ganges is shredded, where it meets the sea, into a tattered labyrinth of islands and spits by the estuaries of rivers large and small. The land is flat and muddy and covered by grey-green jungle. The waters are brown and often treacherous, scoured by fast tidal flows and haunted by that biggest of living reptiles and most dangerous of crocodilians, the salt water crocodile, *Crocodylus porosus*. I had reached the Sundarbans first by travelling overland by buses and battered taxis eastwards to the inland port of Khulna and then south in Karim's hired boat for seventy miles or more, sometimes fast with the tide, sometimes at less than a mile an hour when the tide was against us. Humid heat cocooned the wilderness of monotonous mangrove and the waterways, now broad and gleaming, now narrow, tortuous and dark. Karim claimed to know the forest and its waters since childhood. Head of a large family and in his sixties, he had learned English in the army. He told me that he came for a month each spring, year in year out, to hunt for wild honey in the mangrove forests with six other men from his village. Now, as we chugged and backfired along I watched flocks of flamingoes and storks parading in the shallows and ibises and herons feeding in the mud pools beneath the mangrove trees. Once I glimpsed an Axis deer, its auburn coat and large white spots serving as fine camouflage in a sun-dappled thicket. The boat, a prowed craft of noisily creaking wood, served as my hotel for the three days and two nights it took to reach our destination. Karim cooked three meals a day of rice, peppers and dried fish on a primus stove after tying up at a convenient clump of mangrove roots. Water, warm and with a paraffiny flavour, we carried in jerrycans. At night we hauled the boat half out of the water on to a dry mud bank and slept in it under two layers of mosquito netting. Near the boat Karim kept a fire going throughout the hours of darkness – to deter a visitation by the Great Lord he explained. Before going to sleep he would kneel as a good Moslem and pray towards Mecca and then after declaring his faith in the One God and his prophet would fervently invoke the forest goddess of Hinduism, Banbibi.

'Oh Mother Banbibi, I have come home. Protect me in the forest as a beloved son.' On the second day of the boat journey, we passed several woodcutters' houses built on stilts at the water's edge and once Karim shouted in delight and pointed at something when we were passing through a narrow inlet between two marshy islands.

'See, the honey!' I looked and saw a dead mangrove stump swarming with small bees. 'That will be good honey – white – for the Kolshi mangrove is in flower at this time and the bees love it.'

'Do you get stung often when collecting the honey?' I asked.

'No sir – very rarely. Allah is good to us. My friends and I we hunt together looking for flying bees. Six of us. That is the tradition. We burn torches of green leaves as we go through the forest to quieten the bees and then we follow them as they return to their nests.

'Do none of the men get lost in the forest?'

'No sir. We call constantly to one another like singing birds and the seventh man stays with the boat blowing on this like so.' He picked a large water buffalo horn out of the bilges, put it to his lips and blew a series of mournful hoots.

'And what about the Great Lord or the crocodile – do they never take honey gatherers?'

'Oh sir, it does happen. Even men in a boat have been attacked by Mamaa. But Allah is merciful and I also carry this.' From somewhere inside his shorts he pulled out an amulet in the form of a plastic tiger tooth inscribed with writing and a crude drawing of a deity of some kind. 'Kalu Roy – the Great Lord's Lord!'

At around noon on the third day when I'd have given anything for a pint of cold lager and some steak and kidney pie and we pushed off again after yet another of Karim's rice, pepper and dried fish creations – a dish that he seemed to relish unfailingly – we arrived at a little village of wood and dried mud huts set on a well-drained clearing where the river bank was higher than usual above the water surface.

'We are here, sir!' said Karim, switching off the relieved outboard with an air of proud satisfaction.

'*Where* is *here* Karim?'

'This sir, is Chandpai and we are on the Shela river.' He waved the piece of paper carrying the name of my destination and the purpose of my visit which had been written in Bengali by the vet in Calcutta. 'As instructed, sir, you have been delivered!' Disembarking I did feel rather like a parcel delivered passively to anonymous recipients. Here I was totally without bearings, in a seemingly infinite swamp clinging to the coat-tails of the Indian subcontinent. Without Karim, or if the outboard did what it kept threatening to do, I was as lost as surely as if I'd been parachuted into the Amazonian jungle.

'Come,' said Karim, when he'd moored the boat and

gathered up The Bag and a sack containing supplies, yes, of rice, peppers and dried fish, 'we must find the *dharijals*.'

'What are the *dharijals*?'

'People. Fishermen of very low caste. They have the animals you want to see, sir.'

There were a dozen other small boats moored along the river bank. They were loaded with nets, wicker baskets, rusty tin boxes and cooking pots. Men in dhotis and singlets sat in knots nearby gossiping or crouched over nets spread around them on the ground. The smoke rose up into the hazy white hot sky from small fires outside the houses and everywhere there were gleaming carpets of little fish drying in the sun. The pungent odour of chillies cooking and the earthy smell of the water mixed with that of the drying fish. Talking stopped for a moment when we arrived. The short Bengali fishermen squinted up at me with sharp-eyed curiosity and there were a few giggles as a lean yellow dog smeared in dried mud ran to challenge us barking furiously, its hackles raised. Karim shouted a greeting in Bengali and some of the fishermen raised hands and answered pleasantly enough I reckoned. I could see no sign of otters. My guide spoke again at length to an old man who was squatting and gutting fish on a patch of sunbaked mud. He opened a toothless mouth and gabbled away in a shrill voice while waving his arm in the direction of downstream.

'There are some *dharijal* boats outside the village,' Karim said, 'let us walk – it is not far.'

We walked along the river bank and into the trees by way of a narrow path bordered by reeds. The forest here was thin with an undergrowth of bamboo and creepers. Where the sunlight pierced the mangroves, vines covered in bright red flowers flourished and the air was alive in the traffic of dragonflies, exquisite butterflies and twittering small birds of luminescent dark green and blue.

'It is best that we sing as we go,' murmured Karim, 'because of Mamaa.' In a quavering voice he began to carol, 'Call Allah! Speak his name – it drives away danger. Everything passes and so shall we. Who cares for what vanishes, even if it be the most beautiful Sundari tree -e-e-e-e!'

My anti-tiger chant as we walked was a decidely incongruous 'Widdicombe Fair'. We must have sounded awful – for the Great Lord stayed away!

After about a quarter of a mile among the trees, we came out to where the river bank was again open for a short distance. No houses here, just a bog of grey mud with the forlorn stumps of dead mangroves protruding like rotting teeth. Pop-eyed mudskipper fish had hauled themselves out on to those tree trunks that had pools of water close by and at our approach they stopped their sunbathing and took a dip to be on the safe side. Two long thin boats of black wood lay at the bank. They had decks of lashed bamboo cane which were covered for half their length by low arched shelters built of bamboo and palm leaves. The gunnels were draped with fine nets and had slim black oars hanging in their rowlocks and swinging idly with the stream. A number of bamboo poles projected over one side of each boat, their ends dipping into the water. Eight or nine men were huddled under the shelter of one of the craft eating steaming rice from a communal pan.

'*Dharijals*,' said Karim, 'and they have their . . . what do you call those water-dog animals, sir?'

'Otters.'

'They have their otters with them.' I looked at the boats and the men beneath the shelter and then along the river bank. Still no sign of otters as far as I could see. We walked up to the boats and Karim hailed the *dharijal* fishermen. At once they interrupted their meal and began to scramble ashore. They were thin, serious-looking little men in stained and tattered dhotis and most were naked from the waist up. Their leader appeared to be a grey-haired, cross-eyed individual who was missing two fingers on each hand and had several days' growth of grey stubble on his chin. His name, Karim said, was Bihar and I shook hands with him and all his companions.

'Have you told them why I have come?' I asked my companion.

'Yes. They are very pleased. Very honoured. They did not know there was such a thing as an otter doctor and ask would you like to eat with them.'

'Tell them thank you, no, as we have ourselves just eaten, but please to continue their meal. Afterwards I would like to see the animals.'

The *dharijals* wouldn't hear of it. The rice would wait. I should see the otters at once for two were very sick.

'Where are the otters?' I asked. Karim pointed to the lengths of bamboo jutting out over the boats' sides.

'There sir – in the water. Attached to the ends of the poles.' I looked again. The brown water swirled round the tips of the bamboos and then was suddenly broken by two be-whiskered tawny-coloured heads that emerged through the surface and looked around. Then another head popped up close by, water beads streaming from it like loops of a diamond necklace. Otters! The oriental, small-clawed variety. The three animals looked at us expectantly and I saw immediately that two of them had sore eyes and noses. Both coughed and sneezed from time to time. Each otter was tied by a length of rope which was looped round its neck to the end of one of the bamboo poles. They were tethered as casually as goats in an orchard. Who does not adore otters, apart from psychopaths who hunt these fascinating creatures for sport in Scottish rivers? There are no finer experiences for an animal lover than to watch sea otters in the North Pacific, their toes anchoring them by latching hold of a convenient frond of seaweed, lying on their backs in the sunlight and breaking open abalone shells on their sleek tummies with all the dedication and gusto of the seafood connoisseurs that they are. Or to hide with my friend Terry

Nutkins on a stream near his home on the Isle of Skye and breathlessly observe a European river otter assiduously hunting for eels and crayfish under the glow of a setting sun. Or to conduct an intense conversation of squeaks and whistles with the breeding otters in the zoo pool at Chessington and, when as usual they cajole me into throwing them a hard boiled egg, to see them playing nimbly with it before setting about the cracking of the shell. Or to spend an afternoon just being among otters with otter people in otter country at the marvellous Otter Trust near Bungay in Suffolk. The small-clawed otter is bigger and sturdier than its European relative and possesses insignificant claws, but has plump and sensitive pads on the end of its front 'fingers' with which it deftly roots about in the river bottom and under rocks in search of mussels, snails and fresh water prawns. An alert and inquisitive species like all otters, they can be tamed if artificially reared but tend to have mercurial temperaments and may, in a moment of peak, bite even their best friends with appalling force. Terry Nutkins, a disciple in his youth of Gavin Maxwell, has only eight intact fingers to his name to prove it. I wondered if that was how Bihari lost his missing digits.

'Are they tame otters?' I asked Karim.

'A bit of them is, sir. And a bit is wild.'

To me a bit of wildness in an otter carries the same weight as saying that a girl is a bit pregnant. One of the otters dived and at once resurfaced sneezing violently. Greenish exhudate seeped from its nostrils. Karim explained that the otters 'fish' for their *dharijals* by acting as aquatic sheep dogs, chasing fish towards the men's waiting nets.

'The otters are allowed to eat some fish, but if they get greedy the men pull on the ropes and scold them,' Karim said.

'Can they handle the otters?' I asked. Karim consulted with the men who all shook their heads in that peculiar bobbing Indian fashion that I often confuse with their way of nodding assent.

'No. Too dangerous they say,' replied Karim, 'but the otter doctor can hold them if he wants.' I suppose they assumed I had some special expertise or influence in grabbing semi-wild otters.

'Are those the sick otters?' I asked pointing to the coughing animals in the water.

'No sir. Nothing wrong with them they say. The worst ones have died and the two sick ones are in the other boat.'

'Let me see them.' Two of the fishermen climbed into the second boat and dragged a low bamboo cage out on to the deck. I stepped on board and watched them remove pegs from one side of the cage and flap it down. Lying inside, barely conscious, were two dying otters. They were pitifully thin and had their once elegant coats plastered with excrement. Their eyes and nostrils were caked with congealed pus and a fore leg on one of the animals and a hind leg on the other twitched violently at irregular intervals. One otter was moaning quietly. It was a pitiful, forlorn, keening sound.

'Bihari says they are a great loss,' said Karim over my shoulder, 'such animals are worth at least 2,500 rupees each.'

'How many have died?' I asked.

'This season in Chandpai and the other villages around maybe twelve they think and two more were eaten by crocodiles.' I climbed out of the boat and told Karim to get the fishermen to bring the other otters out of the water for me to look at. Soon the *dharijals* had the water-dripping trio bouncing about at the end of their poles and leashes on the river bank. I crouched down just out of reach of their teeth to see what I could. It was plain that they were all three affected by the same complaint but in a much milder form than the two in the cage. Coughs, sneezes, discharges and hoarse breathing but thankfully no sign yet of any twitches. I stood up and asked Karim to fetch The Bag. There was no doubt what the epidemic was – the *dharijals*' otters had contracted distemper – the disease of your ordinary faithful Fido. The same virus that infects dogs can also produce disease in other animals including otters, mink and even giant pandas. And as in dogs there is no real treatment available even today. Good nursing, control of secondary infections and luck are the only hopes for full recovery. Zoos generally vaccinate valuable susceptible stock against the plague using standard dog vaccines. For VIPs like the pandas, on whom I dare not risk any form of living virus in case it should by a thousand to one chance revert to a wild strain if not for dogs then for pandas, I import specially prepared dead distemper vaccine from Washington DC to be used in Madrid.

'Right,' I said, when I'd found what I wanted in The Bag. 'Get the men to throw some nets over one of the otters. Pile it on. I'm going to give them a jab of medicine.' By wrapping plenty of net round the animals we should be protected long enough from their teeth for me to get an injection of long-acting sulphonamide into a muscle through the mesh. It was a rough, tough way of handling a sick animal but there was no alternative. Bihari brought the nets and after one of his men shortened the length of rope on an otter by winding it round the end of the pole, he threw a net over the protesting creature. Otters are powerful, incredibly agile fellows and in a flash it had somehow wriggled out, squeaking indignantly, from underneath. It needed several more tries and two more nets before we had it pinned and probably a bit short of air. I located the position of the head and associated weaponry and then poked my fingers through the net at the other end. I found a bit of straining muscular flesh and stuck my needle in.

'OK, let him go!' I shouted. We treated the other two animals in the same way and all the otters survived their rather suffocating ordeal. When it was done I gave the *dharijals* all the ampicillin capsules I was carrying as a precaution against Delhi belly and other travellers' ailments. 'Tell them to put the capsules in a fish through the gills and give them each day to the otters,' I instructed Karim. I had no hope for the two animals in the cage and would have euthanased them if I had been carrying any suitable drug. One of the great things about being a zoo vet is that I so rarely have to put animals down. Unlike the vet in general practice, euthanasia solutions are not part of the armamentarium carried regularly in The Bag. On this occasion I regretted it. For what it was worth, I gave the two moribund animals in the cage a shot of sulpha and also a stiff dose of valium. They were utterly unaware of the needle prick. But what about all the other *dharijals* of the Sundarbans and their fishing otters? Something had to be done to try to control the epidemic.

'Ask how many otters they think the *dharijals* of these parts own,' I said. There was much thought and some argument before Bihari came up with a figure of a probable fifty.

'And all the *dharijals* more or less know one another or are related or meet in the fishing villages from time to time?'

'Yes sir, we are from the same few families,' came the reply.

'Good – then do you think you could inject otters like I did if I sent some medicine?' Much conferring but eventually they decided that they could. I showed them how to put a syringe and needle together and how to make up a solution by mixing a vial of sterile saline with a bottle of freeze dried powder. For demonstration purposes I used water with some liver extract powder. 'You will do the same,' I told them through Karim, 'for I will see that you receive a special medicine, water and powder to be mixed together before injecting, to protect all your otters.'

'There is no postman in the Sundarbans,' Karim muttered. 'How will they receive the medicine?'

'I will send sixty doses to the post office of Khulna in your name Karim,' I replied. 'Then when you come here to collect honey at the end of March, you can deliver them.' My Pekinese-faced friend smiled, 'And you will send me also an English tie?' he said.

'A tie! – what do you want a tie for?'

'The officers in the army. They used them sir, in the mess at night. I would very much like one – with stripes!'

'Done,' I said laughing, 'you will have *two* ties Karim with stripes and when you get me back to Khulna 1,000 rupees, as well as a bonus for delivering the medicines.'

Later in the afternoon, as the sun plunged like an ingot for tempering into a bank of dense clouds on the horizon and the first bat sallied forth from the mangroves, the time of low tide came round and the two boats and their crews of men and three otters pushed off into mid-stream, the men singing and the otters porpoising through the water on their leashes. A hundred yards down stream they began to fish. First, the men dipped their rectangular nets fixed in a light bamboo frame into the water, then there was a flurry as the otters dived and herded an invisible shoal of fish over their submerged net. When they judged the time right, the men flipped the net up sending a glinting cascade of sardine-sized fish on to the deck. Quickly they dipped the net again. Dip, flip. Dip, flip. Men and otters with the latter no doubt feverish from their infection, worked steadily until the light was almost gone.

'Tonight the fishermen want to give you a feast sir,' said Karim, as the two boats were finally moored for the night and the otters were left, still roped, to fend for themselves hunting beneath the boats for shellfish or if they wished resting up on the decks. By the light of a mangrove wood fire with clouds of mosquitos about our heads and the bats skimming through the glow of the flames, we dined – on rice peppers and dried fish, proudly cooked into a kedgeree by our *dharijal* hosts. Later that night when I stripped to my underpants before crawling under the mosquito nets to sleep in our boat, I found a bloated land leech that had almost certainly sneaked under my trouser bottoms while we walked through the forest, firmly fixed to my ankle. It was my first personal encounter with one of these sophisticated and immensely interesting parasites. I detached it by pushing at its mouth parts with my thumbnail and it fell into the bilges. The neat Y-shaped wound oozed persistently for two days before clotting.

Three days later I was back in bustling rundown Khulna. I paid off Karim who somewhere located a dozen cans of warm beer to sustain me on my journey, gave him his bonus and took a taxi to the Pakistan border.

'Don't forget the tie sir!' he shouted as I waved goodbye. I didn't. Pentland Hick arranged for five dozen Epivax distemper vaccines to be sent to Karim by express airmail soon after I returned. In the parcel I included two striped ties. Karim, wherever he is in the Sundarbans if the Great Lord or irate bees or crocodiles haven't got him and he hasn't marooned himself in the wilderness, can at least *claim* to be both ex-Household cavalry *and* an Old Etonian, should that count for anything much among the workers of the mangrove forest. To the best of my knowledge the bulk of the otters in the region survived for they are certainly still busily fishing there alongside the kindly *dharijals*.

12 Dragons and Unicorns

'Listen to voices in the upper air, nor lose thy simple faith in mysteries' – *Longfellow*. People are enthralled by the idea of mysteries, undiscovered animals and none more so than I. 'Ah,' folk like me say when the ancient fables of dragons and minotaurs and dog-headed men are once more retold. 'There's no smoke without fire you know!' And we may well be right. Within living memory one big mammal, the okapi, was discovered living in the dense rain forests of the Congo. Recent reports of dinosaurs being seen in the same region have sent scientists of the International Society of Cryptozoology (the study and investigation of undiscovered species), of which I am a member, out to investigate. Don't grin! Remember, the massive Steller's sea cow was originally discovered in 1741 and wiped out at man's hand almost certainly by 1768. But reports of sightings of animals which *might* have been some of these bigger relatives of the mannatee and dugong came from Russian sailors in the lonely waters off Cape Navarin in 1963. The dodo, that ridiculous-looking flightless giant pigeon famed in *Alice in Wonderland*, was found early in the sixteenth century and was extinct within a century or so. But Latimeria, the coelocanth, a fish with primitive legs and which is of major significance in the study of evolutionary processes, was first fished out of the ocean in 1938. Since then many more have been caught – it was just a matter of knowing where and how deep to look! The Takahe, a flightless bird, was thought to be no longer an inhabitant of the planet until 100 birds of the species were rediscovered in 1948 in a remote mountain area of New Zealand. The Quagga, a member of the zebra family, lived in Africa until 1861 and in European zoos as late as 1883. But were some sighted in Ovamboland in 1920? A few weeks ago it was confirmed that the Thylacine, the marsupial dog of Australia and thought to be gone for ever, was still around, alive and well in Tasmania. Every year zoologists come across literally hundreds of species of smaller creatures, insects and other invertebrates (a giant bee, for example, found in 1984 in South America) which are unknown to science and do not come to the attention of the average man on the Clapham omnibus or make headlines in the newspapers.

With monotonous regularity some sort of 'monster' scare occurs in Great Britain – pumas on the loose in Surrey woods or the Beast of Dartmoor; home grown and slightly down-market equivalent of the North American Big Foot and the Himalayan yeti mysteries. Sadly – and I've been involved in investigating a number of them, lying in wait with a dart gun, post-morteming victims and taking plaster casts of spoor – the British big cat always turns out to be a Great Dane or a Dobermann Pinscher. And the numerous sea monsters that I have examined on lonely stretches of shore up and down our coasts have without exception proved to be the bizarre effects of putrefaction acting on the corpses of sharks, whales and, very occasionally, oarfish. But I'm still a believer in unknown animals. By extrapolating the graphs of frequency of discovery of new species over the past years, it strikes me as statistically certain that in the vast unexplored areas of the oceans, the deep forests of South America, parts of the Far East, the mountains and the deserts of Soviet Asia and the Himalayas, there must be thousands – as yet unseen and unnamed – of invertebrates, hundreds of fish, dozens of birds and small mammals and one or two big mammals and reptiles waiting for us. Monsters round the corner!

And as well as all that, I derive much pleasure from knowing that Britain itself still possesses wild animals which, choosing to live in certain habitats, are to the public at large essentially unknown and undiscovered. The Surrey puma is dead – long live the Scottish wild cat! *Felis sylvestris*, the fierce and secretive hunter – not a domestic cat gone feral like the moggies of Venice or derelict inner city areas, but as real a wild and magnificent a cat as the tiger or jaguar – still dwells in the quiet forests of the Highlands. And I rejoice in the immigrants among our wild life who have successfully made their homes in Britain in recent times and who surprisingly thrive and reproduce contentedly in our alien climate. Some of these again are rarely spotted by folk walking or driving through the countryside. The most elusive and welcome for me are the wallabies now well established in the Derbyshire Peak District.

It struck me the other day, when someone brought up the subject of mythical animals in conversation, that as a peripatetic zoo vet I was unique in having had as patients unicorns, dragons, mermaids and vampires. Not to mention the stuffed Big-Foot that I'd been called to give an opinion on at Blackpool (a fraud) and the great 1969 Loch Ness monster hunt, where I'd been in charge of chemical baiting and biopsy dart-gunning should the expedition succeed in forcing our Nessie to surface. The fabulous creatures of universal fairy tales are in many ways based upon man's ancient encounters with and exaggerated reporting of flesh and blood beasts – which are alive today! And occasionally need veterinary attention!

The unicorn is perhaps the most famous of all fantastic fauna. It was (or is!) an animal of magical powers which according to classical writers can be easily caught by leaving a young virgin alone in the forest. Eventually the unicorn is bound to appear and, gently laying his head in her lap, will consent to be taken captive. Marco Polo actually claimed on returning from his Far Eastern travels to have seen lots of unicorns. His description of them as 'ugly brutes with the hair of buffalo and elephant's feet' is markedly different from the traditional portrait of these wonderous one-horned horses. Almost certainly Marco was referring to the Indian or Sumatran rhinoceros which he'd come across. Of course, the most magical bit of a unicorn is its horn – and still today millions of people in the Far East believe in the special properties of rhinoceros horn. African poachers kill rhino just to steal the horn and sell it to merchants in Hong Kong or Bangkok. You'll see such horns (actually composed of compressed masses of skin hair, but hard as teak) in most apothecarys' shops in the Far East on sale at enormous prices. The horn is grated like a nutmeg and the resulting powder taken in water or a little wine as a sure remedy for sexual problems.

I've treated many rhinoceroses all over the world – they are hardy animals in zoos and safari parks and the square-lipped or white rhino quickly becomes as manageable as a domestic cow – loving to have its skin scratched and snuffling around one's person for titbits. The major disease problems of the rhino are stomach upsets and skin ailments. Perhaps more frequently than for anything else on the surgical side, I am called to sort out rhino who have damaged their horns in some way. After fighting or accidents, the impressive horn has been deeply split or partly or even completely broken off at the base. With a tame animal I can, using a surform plane, chisels and a selection of files trim a split horn, make grooves to stop the split extending and generally tidy up the animal's proud possession. No sedatives are needed for there are no nerves in the horn itself. If the horn has been uprooted or partially severed at the base I need to dope this living chieftain tank first. That means slapping a needle into the buttocks and then to ensure it penetrates the very thick tough skin (much more formidable than that of an elephant) clouting it home with a hammer before injecting a little M99 anaesthetic. If the horn has to be amputated it will grow again slowly but rarely to anything of any size. Zoos and safari parks, I am pleased to say, *don't* sell any broken horns or horns taken from dead rhino to the Far East – no one wants to encourage the superstitious trade in bits of beasts' bodies. But I don't regard the rhinoceros as the main origin of the unicorn legend.

Unicorn horns (alicorns) were considered invaluable items in any European physician's pharmacopoeia right up to the beginning of the nineteenth century. No apothecary, no doctor was without at least a bit of one. They were worth around three times their weight in gold even if they didn't look at all like rhino horns! They were creamy white, twisted into a spiral and often several feet long. You can still see such an alicorn in the Science Museum's Department of Medical History in London. Where did these precious horns come from? For they are and were undoubtedly not artefacts but portions of an animal's natural anatomy. The answer lies in the icy waters of the Arctic for here be, not monsters, but a truly wonderful and little known mammal – the whale we call the Narwhal. The Narwhal grows up to about 4 metres long and feeds mainly on squid but also takes cod, flat fish and shellfish. It possesses only two teeth in the upper jaw, one of which in the male (generally it is the left-hand tooth for some reason) grows forward in an anti-clockwise spiral to a length of two metres or more. This 'horn' can thus be half or even two-thirds the length of the rest of the body. You can see that there are fundamental structural differences between the horn of an animal like a deer which is composed of solid keratin, the compressed hair of rhino horn and the tooth ivory of a Narwhal horn. What is the purpose of the Narwhal's amazing denture? We don't know. Certainly a secondary sexual characteristic, it may be part of his ritual armoury and sometimes a practical weapon. It may just be a bit of spectacular dandyism by eligible Narwhal men-about-town in search of impressionable mates. More interestingly some scientists think that the horn may also be used as a sound probe, a sort of aerial for picking up sound including sonar waves. Sound conduction pathways through the skull from the jaw to the inner ear are known to exist in other members of the whale and dolphin family.

Narwhals have virtually never been exhibited in marinelands. We have often discussed it but the risk of breaking the fairly brittle Narwhal horn during transport is considerable. No, I've never had a Narwhal as a patient but I've been privileged to see one that my colleague, Doctor Jay Hyman of New York Aquarium, brought back from an expedition to Alaska. An orphan baby, it was rescued by Jay but sadly died despite the enormous expertise and dedication that was employed in trying to raise it artificially. Other than that the closest I've got to a Narwhal, a memorable moment, was when I was in Narssassuak, Greenland in November 1969. A family group of six Narwhals, among which was a magnificent male toting a 1½-metre long horn, cruised down the coast while I was there. To see that unicorn lancing the icy indigo water against a snow laden pewter sky was, yes, magical.

But the ancient fables of the unicorn seem to have originated in the East. I cannot believe that the Narwhal was at the root of them. True, one-horned animals with proper horns do not exist and as far as we can tell from fossil records never have existed. Scientists have transplanted the horn buds of young calves to the centre of the head and thus surgically engineered a unicorn which, there is some evidence to suggest, became subsequently the dominant herd leader over its normal two-horned fellows. David Attenborough has proposed that this technique, not particularly complex, was known to the ancients and that they thereby produced 'unicorns' to use in subjugating and controlling herds of animals for human exploitation. Perhaps, but I doubt it. Again no fossil evidence. A more likely candidate for 'Mr Unicorn', however, is the Arabian oryx, that most handsome of antelopes, white of coat with black markings and superb tapering sword-like horns. This animal, seen from the side, particularly in the shimmering white heat of the deserts of Arabia, often appears to have just one horn, so symmetrically set are its pair of lethal appendages. I have to look after many such unicorns in the Arabian Gulf in collections from Qatar to Abu Dhabi to Dubai and including one individual, Ibn Soorah, who *may* have been the last surviving wild caught male, for the oryx, despite occasional reports to the contrary from Bedou in the Empty Quarter, is probably extinct in its ancient haunts. My involvement with the Arabian oryx has been many-faceted. Called to epidemics of Pasteurella infections transmitted by pigeons from herds of nomadic goats, to suspected outbreaks of the dread virus pestilence, Rinderpest, to move animals from A to B under anaesthetic, to mend all manner of halt and maimed individuals and to deliver oryx cows in difficulties at the moment of birth, I have developed a deep admiration for this tough noble animal which can survive the heat and desolation of the waterless, food-sparse deep desert.

Last year in Qatar, I was asked to examine a sheik's private herd of oryx which were all showing grey-blue bald patches in their normally matchless white coats. With difficulty in his immense desert paddocks I darted one animal using a tranquillising rifle. When it was sleeping I put a magnifying glass to the bald areas but could see nothing significant. I scratched off some bits of the upper layers of skin with the back of a scalpel blade, put them in a test-tube and took them with me back to London. There the skin scales were examined under the microscope by a veterinary parasitologist friend in Weybridge. The powerful lenses revealed hosts of minute cigar-shaped creatures, mange mites of the *Demodex* family. (The same parasite lives in the eyelash hair follicles of most human beings!) How to treat oryx in a vast area of fenced dune desert for mange? No question of shampooing, spraying or dipping, the methods you would use with a dog or a sheep. Luckily a new injectable anti-mange drug, ivermectin, had just been developed for use in farm animals. I decided to try it, not by injection – too tricky – but by mouth in the oryx. To get the oryx to eat it I diluted the ivermectin, which doesn't taste very nice, in top quality first pressing olive oil (the Oil of the Virgin) and sent it out to Qatar with instructions for it to be mixed with whole barley and fed to the affected herd. This was done and after three weeks I received a telex saying that it had apparently worked perfectly. The Arabian oryx had got over their bald spots! Would that I could so easily! Rhinoceros, Narwhal, Arabian oryx – take your pick. Is one of them the real unicorn or could there be perhaps. . .?

Now let us turn to the sinister subject of vampires. Shades of Bela Lugosi, Boris Karloff and the Count Dracula. Victims drained of blood, monsters who must be abed by sunrise, wooden stakes driven through undead hearts – it's all chilling, delicious stuff on the back row of the Odeon or as late night Hammer video on TV. But there *are* stealthy nocturnal bloodsuckers *for real*! I'm not referring to those occasional cases in criminal psychopathology where a perverted desire to drink the blood of other humans is manifested, nor to the many invertebrate bloodsuckers such as fleas, lice, parasitic bugs, mosquitos, nematode worms and the famous medicinal leech. No. *The* vampire, flying by night, sleeping by day, subtle and secretive and surviving only by drinking warm blood, is a bat. The vampire bat of Tropical America and the Caribbean.

The true vampire bats feed exclusively on the blood of warm-blooded animals including man and rarely if ever drink water, getting all their liquid requirements from their gory meals. Alighting gently on their prey, they may fan their wings to generate a soothing draught of cool air while cutting through the skin with two very sharp V-shaped upper incisor teeth. The cut is so fine, rather like that of a razor blade, that it tends to clot very slowly and the bat assists the flow of blood by licking the wound frequently. As with the leech there are anti-clotting chemicals in the saliva. The vampire doesn't actually 'suck' blood but rather laps it up and the incisions made tend to bleed for many hours afterwards. When I first began working at Belle Vue the nearby University Medical School kept a small colony of vampire bats for research on aspects of the anti-clotting saliva and I was called in whenever necessary to keep them fit and healthy. The bats were maintained in strict quarantine, indeed the principal reason why there are no vampire bats at all in captivity in the United Kingdom at the present time is because by law they must now be housed under permanent quarantine because of their tendency to carry rabies virus within their body. Feeding the bats was done by obtaining cows' blood from the abattoir, stirring it vigorously with a kitchen whisk to drag out the clots and then pouring the liquid into shallow glass dishes. The bats who drank half to two-thirds of their body weight in blood each day didn't seem to care whether their liquid lunches were served warm or chilled straight from the fridge. I remember well my first confrontation with a vampire that needed medical attention.

The laboratory was in the basement of a hospital on Oxford Road. I was shown into the room where the bats were kept in a large glass cubicle with double doors, on the outer one of which was printed DANGER: VAMPIRE QUARANTINE: STRICTLY NO ENTRY! in large crimson letters. The interior of the cubicle was dimly lit by a purple bulb and I could see maybe two dozen darkish bats hanging from a false roof of wire mesh which served as their 'roost'. They were much smaller than I had imagined weighing perhaps 30 grams and with a wing span at full extension of no more than 25 centimetres. 'Right,' said the lab technician who was in charge of them, after I'd changed into rubber overalls and wellingtons, 'I suppose you want to grab one or two.' He thrust a pair of thick leather gloves towards me. 'Put these on. The little buggers bite like nobody's business. You don't want hydrophobia, I reckon.' I certainly did not fancy catching hydrophobia (rabies) which can be transmitted through the tiniest scratch contaminated by saliva from a bat carrying but showing no symptoms of this most serious brain disease. At the time, I wasn't vaccinated as I am now against rabies and the vaccination system then employed, and usually only on suspect cases in human beings, was the old and highly unpleasant one of a series of injections into the abdomen.

'Hold on a minute!' I said. 'What's supposed to be wrong with them?'

'Didn't the Prof tell you on the 'phone?'

'Nobody gave me any details. Just that some of the bats were off colour.'

The technician shook his head and tut-tutted. 'Aye well – this lot came a week ago from Mexico. They started off heartily enough, right bloody guzzlers and no mistake but over the past couple of days they've stopped feeding and are looking a lot thinner. Do you know owt about 'em?'

I'd never seen a vampire bat before let alone treated one. But I had read something about their commoner ailments and I'd already had experience with several other sorts of bats, principally the fruit eating varieties such as the flying fox. Not wanting to seem utterly green to the technician I answered, 'A thing or two!' and nodded what I hoped looked like a very wise nod. I went through the double doors, disinfecting my boots in a bath of antiseptic and stood looking up at the hanging bats. The upside-down flitter-mice twittered nervously at my presence and clambered awkwardly away from me. It smelt awful in there. After checking my gloves had no holes in them I made a grab at one of the nearest and thinnest-looking individuals. While it squeaked in outrage and bit determinedly into the glove fingers, I unpicked the grip of its claws on the wire with my other hand and brought it down on to a convenient ledge within the cubicle where I could examine it by the light of a spotlamp shone through the glass by the technician outside. I put the bat on to the ledge and stood back to appraise it. I'm sorry to say that its appearance and demeanour really were in keeping with the malign reputation appropriate to a familiar of demons. It stood awkwardly and bent on all fours, by that I mean on its hind feet and the thumbs of its wings, with an expression of glinting malevolence suffusing its tiny flat-nosed face. The largish black eyes fixed me intently and the mouth snarled, half-open, with the two famous cutting teeth just visible. Presently it began to move crabwise away from me down the ledge, first with a gait that reminded me strongly of a bird-eating spider and then by clumsy hops, wings outspread. The horror film had got it right! Before it could launch itself into the air or fall off I seized hold of it again. Gently I stretched it out and peered at the furry grey-brown body. I noticed a few black fleas hurrying for cover but little else. Breathing and pulse rates, racing away under my finger tips as the animal struggled in panic, provided no information. The bat was thin all right and I got the impression that its eyelids seemed to be drooping rather unnaturally and there was a light rash under the belly fur. Otherwise, I could find nothing remarkable. I released the bat and went outside.

'I'll take a blood smear from one,' I told the technician. 'You'll have to come in and hold it while I do it.' He put on his set of rubber overalls and came with me into the cubicle. While he held another thin bat I snipped the very tip off one of its foreclaws and let a drop of blood ooze out. This I smeared on to a glass microscope slide and let dry into a film.

'Hah!' sniggered my companion. 'You can call yourself a vampire's vampire now, eh!'

'OK let it go,' I said. 'I'd like to have a look at this slide before deciding what we should do.' I'd taken the blood smear rather than a full sample because I didn't at that time know how, without doing a cardiac puncture which might have been fatal in such a nervous little creature, to bleed a bat. While holding the first bat I was unable to raise the jugular vein in its neck through the thick clumsy gloves. As a young vet I did not relish making a fool of myself in front of a hospital technician by struggling with multiple needle prods to find an elusive and possibly non-existent blood vessel! Vampire bat anatomy books, as you might imagine, are rarer than first folio Shakespeares. But the blood smear might yield some useful information, for a differential white cell count and examination of the red cells would be possible. Using the lab's own facilities, I stained the smear in the usual way with coloured dyes, rinsed and dried it, applied a drop of special oil and then put it under a microscope. Focusing the instrument I looked down the eyepiece at the white field of light strewn with red discs and white and blue amoeba-shapes which is the typical appearance of a mammalian – human or vampire bat – bloodfilm. Everything looked normal until suddenly, as I twiddled the knobs that moved the slide slowly up and down and left to right, I spied a beautiful purple veil. It wasn't very big but there it lay, an elegant twist and curl of what might have been silk, a scarf dropped by a fashionable lady or forgotten by her where she'd left it draped over a handful of red cells. Galvanised, I moved the slide hurriedly around and soon found two other pretty purple scarves.

'Come and look at this!' I shouted to the technician. He peered down the microscope. 'D'you know what they are' I asked, 'those bits of purple?'

'No.'

'Those my friend are trypanosomes – sleeping sickness!'

The twists of colour were blood parasites, the sort that cause sleeping sickness in man and similar diseases in other species. The bats, before they left South America, had been feeding on something or somebody with trypanosomes in their blood. It might well have been horses with the Mal de Caderas disease – known to exist in that part of the world though not in Britain. Seeing the parasite didn't prove that they were the cause of the bats' sickness. They could be just carriers of the bugs – perhaps had been for years, for vampire bats can live as long as domestic dogs. But, suppose the stress of capture, transport and a new environment had turned a dormant carrier state into active disease. With nothing else to explain the outbreak of illness, I decided to have a crack at the trypanosomes using drugs normally employed in humans for sleeping sickness. Vampires – sleeping sickness – the long dead monster napping for years in his coffin; could reality be mimicking the myth again?

At that moment I glanced at my right hand and my stomach seemed to do a somersault. I was bleeding slightly from a tiny scratch at the base of the thumb. The gloves – there must have been a hole through which the teeth of one of the bats had managed to reach me! Suppose the rabies virus was already nestling in my flesh! Sweating faintly I grabbed the gloves I had just discarded and searched intently for any gaps in the leather. I found none, but when I turned the right hand glove inside out I discovered a smudge of blood on a ridged seam of badly cured hard leather just where the thumb joined the palm. No hole. I gave a loud sigh of relief.

The head of the department almost had a heart attack when I told him what I'd found and showed him my blood smear, but he agreed that an attempt at treatment should be made with the animals safely confined as they were in quarantine. He also arranged for a supply of the latest anti-trypanosome drug to be sent over at once from the Liverpool School of Tropical Medicine. When it arrived I had to guess at a dose rate for the stuff by taking a bat's weight as about one four-thousandth of an adult human and hoping that with regard to the drug the bat physiology had no special differences from that of man. I injected each bat with the new remedy and repeated the dose after four days. To my relief none of the vampires reacted badly to the treatment and what was more they began to eat a little on the day following the first shot. Thereafter they continued a slow return to normal weight and behaviour. Two months later when I made more blood smears, there was not a single pretty purple silk scarf anywhere to be found! With the trypanosomes apparently successfully exorcised, my first professional encounter with vampires came to a satisfactory conclusion. I often think of them, most appropriately, when I am enjoying a plump steamed Lancashire Black Pudding for supper and it's dark outside with the wind whistling . . .

Orpheus' lute was supposed to 'make tigers tame and huge leviathans forsake unbounded deeps to dance on sands' according to Shakespeare in *Two Gentlemen of Verona*. Leviathan, the sea monster, the kraken, things that go bump in the briny – what of them? Well, leviathan, that marine giant mentioned in the Bible and by numerous ancient writers as well as Shakespeare, would seem to refer to the whale and I've got a bunch of them on my panel of patients. They really do love music too and sometimes we use it as a therapeutic aid during convalescence. No blue or sperm whales yet, but belugas, pilots, killers and false killers – leviathans right enough but none longer than about 10 metres – I've treated them all and written about them and their doctoring elsewhere. But there are other monsters of the sea – serpents, sea-going crocodiles, the great sharks and one that is surely the real live kraken of legend, the giant squid, *Architeuthis*. This overgrown version of the humble calamar that goes so well with garlic and hot oil and cold Retsina wine can be 60 feet in length with 35-foot arms and a weight of 2 tons. No, I still expectantly await my first call to an *Architeuthis*, but I have had professional dealings with one of his relatives, a giant in his own right, *Octopus apollyon* – the Giant Red Pacific octopus. This impressive mollusc comes from the cold waters of the North Pacific and makes your little camouflaged Mediterranean octopus look positively dull by comparison. The red mottled skin which goes even redder when the animal is agitated, the big black and gold eyes and the bulk of the animal (53 kilos in weight is the record with 9-metre long tentacles) combine to make this, the largest of all octopus species, a fiercely dramatic-looking character.

I brought several into the United Kingdom from Seattle in the 1960s, and had to wrestle with the difficulties of keeping the animals cool enough and of stopping them poisoning themselves by their own excreta when confined in a plastic bag together with a little sea water and a lot of oxygen during the journey. After the long flight from Seattle, during which time I could not get at the octopuses as they were in the cargo hold, sealed in their bags, I had to look at them and start reviving and refreshing them as soon as possible. When we landed at Heathrow I would hurriedly unpack them, drain out the water, replenish it and pipe cool oxygen to them. Octopuses of such a size are understandably difficult to handle, not that they charge at you roaring and biting (they are far too intelligent and sensitive animals for that) but because they are so slippery and sloppy. It's like trying to lift a half hundredweight or more of quicksilver with your bare hands. They literally flow through your fingers and the cargo handlers at Heathrow were generally loath to help – and even more so after one of their number thought that I brought him within an ace of death at the hands, all eight of them, of the Creature from the Black Lagoon.

It happened with the second octopus that I imported. The TWA flight had been delayed by a long technical stop at New York and when the octopus arrived at London I was deeply worried about the possible build up of toxins in its system. As soon as it was brought into the cargo shed in the freight village I jemmied open the outer box, removed the insulating wads of paper and slit the thick plastic inner bag to come face to face with a very, very red, very brassed off giant octopus. Knowing the sophisticated nervous system and the eye that is designed so incredibly much like a human's, in these creatures, I found myself talking to it in a soothing reassuring voice just as one might gentle a dog or a pony in a similar situation. Whatever it thought of my blandishments it wasn't saying for it at once began to heave itself liquidly out of the bag and over the edge of the box – around 70 pounds of muscular jelly that had one blindingly obvious message for me and the world at large to ponder – I'M OFF! My first consideration, however, as its mighty vermilion mantle hove into view and one rheumy eye regarded me with cold impatience, was that the monster's colour apart from being angry was rather unhealthy. What the octopus needed was to lie quietly while I let oxygen flow over him and showered him with my portable spray bottle of sea water. And I wanted to inject one of the tentacles with vitamin B complex to assist in breaking down accumulated poisons. The octopus, though, had other ideas as it began to ooze like so much fiery lather over the warehouse floor. A group of cargo handlers stood a little way off cheering me on but incomprehensibly rooted to their respective spots as I tried in vain to talk, and I suppose the best word is 'slurp', portions of the protean beast back into its container.

'Can someone *please* give me a hand?' I called in my best 'no-need-to-worry-ha-ha-ha-isn't-he-a-card?' tone of voice. Rising panic is another word for it. 'I want to give, er, Melvin, here a shot of medicine and stuff him back in.' There was a general guffaw.

'Stuff Melvin!' shouted a man in distant voice. No volunteers came forth. The newly christened Melvin was now nine-tenths out and running – in the way unset jelly runs – for cover. Apoplectic to the tips of his tentacles that constantly changed the subtle distribution of scarlet pigment blotches over their surfaces as if swept by blazing winds, he had the eye that wasn't monitoring me fixed on a brand new racing bicycle, labelled but without packing, which was standing against a pillar nearby. The octopus flowed up to it and then up it.

'He's going to ride off lads!' shouted someone in great glee. And for a moment it looked like it. I had a brief vision of a Giant Red Pacific octopus pedalling hard with two arms down the M4 while two steered and two more gave all sorts of direction signs. The last two would be reserved for giving me, panting along behind, a very big red V sign. But no, Melvin started to flow through the back wheel of the bike. Crack! He flexed his muscles a bit and a shiny spoke sprang loose.

'For God's sake give me a hand!' I yelled, as the only octopus never to win the Tour de France insinuated a portion of itself between the chain and the bicycle's frame. In a moment, disentangling an octopus from a bicycle would necessitate taking the machine to bits. A red-faced, middle-aged man with a generous beer belly under his bib and brace emerged from the growing knot of cargo handlers. His friends cheered as he walked over but stayed where they were.

'Good on you, Wally!' they brayed. Wally had a sheepish grin as he arrived beside me.

'I keep tropical fish meself,' he said 'Something like this is a bit out of my league.'

'Look I'll try to uncoil the tentacles and tease them out. You hold the bulk of the animal back!' I said. Wally rolled up his sleeves and reluctantly slipped both hands into Melvin's irate mass. Ping! Another spoke went but that gave me more room and I managed to withdraw one of the tentacles. Its suckers attached themselves firmly to my wrist. With that limb temporarily immobilised I had to continue the unpicking one-handed. 'Pull him away!' I said. Wally began dragging Melvin towards the box when he suddenly let out an almighty yell and jumped back waving an arm in the air.

'Aaaaagh! It's got me!' he hollered. 'Bloody hell, it's got me!' I looked up. Blood dripped from one of Wally's fingers. Melvin had indeed bitten him. At once pale as cheese, Wally buckled at the knees and crashed to the floor – mercifully not on top of my octopus. The other men stopped their chortling and came running over.

'What's happened? How did it do it? Hey watch it, Doc, let's get Wally out of here before he has another go!'

They skirted widely round the quivering Melvin and pulled their companion clear. Someone loosened his shirt collar. I struggled on alone with the octopus and tried to reassure the cargo handlers. 'He must have put his hand near the animal's beak. They can bite quite hard.'

'You should have warned him!' muttered one of the men slapping the fated Wally on the cheeks. Another fellow was inspecting the damaged finger.

'It's only a little cut,' he declared. 'Nothing much.' Wally came round and sat up as I, puffing with the exertion, shuffled on my bottom across the floor, most of Melvin embracing me clammily.

'Oooh!' moaned the injured party as he looked at his finger. 'Do something lads. It's stinging like hell. Get the ambulance for God's sake. It's bitten me!'

'Don't fret Wally,' said one of his mates. 'It's nothing but a cut!'

'It's the poison – that's what'll kill me! It's the poison! Dial 999! Get the quack!' he closed his eyes and laid back, going pale again.

'Better 'phone the ambulance like he says,' said someone and a man ran off.

'Is it true they're poisonous then, Doc?'

'Well, as a matter of fact they are,' I replied. 'But this sort shouldn't cause much more than a painful swelling.' Thank goodness, I thought, that Wally hadn't been punctured by the small and very pretty blue-ringed octopus found in Australian waters. It has venom that has been known to kill a man within two hours of a tiny bite on the back of the neck. Giant reds weren't in that class. By the time the ambulance arrived, Wally had come round again and was looking lugubriously at his finger that was oozing blood and debating quietly with his colleagues, gathered in a circle around him, whether a priest to perform the last rites should also be summoned. With Melvin in my lap I sat on the floor nearby and tried in vain to assure everybody that Wally was not in trouble, let alone going to expire. At least the octopus was now off its bike but I needed help if I was going to get him into the bag and the box. No one had the slightest intention of helping me. Their occasional glances in my direction were reproachful. In their eyes I was the lunatic with the lethal, loaded monster about his person. If one were daft enough to fancy scrabbling about on freight shed floors with half-crazed octopuses, one should be left to get on with it. When the ambulance arrived, Wally bade his farewells with tears in his eyes and was loaded on to a stretcher.

'A rum job isn't it?' said one ambulance man after they had stowed him away and he came over to look at Melvin and me, getting nowhere. 'What are you going to do with that horror?' he asked.

'Well,' I replied despairingly. 'We've decided to sit here until one of us dies of exhaustion or starvation!'

'You're kidding,' said the ambulance man his eyes widening. 'It's not some sort of a sit-in is it?'

'With an octopus?' I gritted. 'No! All I want is some *help*!' The ambulance man called his colleague.

'Hey George, bring that spare stretcher over here!' What a sensible fellow. With the stretcher laid on the ground beside me I somehow managed to unload Melvin on to it.

'For God's sake, you're not bringing that bastard to hospital as well are you?' groaned Wally from within the ambulance as he watched us.

When Melvin was more or less on the stretcher, the ambulance men carried him over to the box and I scraped, prised, cajoled, wheedled, pushed, shoved and slopped the beast into the container. The ambulance pulled away and I went to work on my patient with the injection and the oxygen while Wally sped towards his doom.

Melvin survived his ordeal and so did Wally. The cargo handler was discharged, his finger covered in elastoplast, after an hour's rest at the hospital. Little if any of the octopus's saliva had entered the wound. I sent him a bottle of whisky in appreciation of his gallantry with Melvin's and my apologies and received a charming letter in reply, saying that he'd been given a fearful wigging by his wife when he arrived home that evening. She'd accused him of falling down when drunk after hearing his likely story. Imagine listening to, 'You'll never guess what happened to me at work today, dear. Well, I was bitten by a big red octopus . . .

The glamour slot in the world of fairy marine zoology is undoubtedly occupied by that most beauteous of fish or finny of females, the mermaid – a seductive, silver-voiced damsel often to be seen with a comb and a mirror in her hands. Mary Queen of Scots was given the nickname 'Mermaid' because of her great beauty and Shakespeare in *A Midsummer Night's Dream*, is referring to her and her marriage to the Dauphin of France when he makes Oberon say 'thou remember'st since once I sat upon a promontory and heard a mermaid on a dolphin's back'. Belle Vue's funfair, not long before it closed, had a 'mermaid' sideshow of a species popular with mountebanks and carnival men since the eighteenth century. A spotty girl from Oldham with a perpetually running nose, who had also been the 'spider woman' and the 'talking head' in previous seasons, lay in a glass case with the lower half of her body fitted into a snakeskin tube that tapered to a cellophane tail fin. Her long wig ever draped coyly over her breasts, she spent her time reading *Titbits* and pulling insolent faces at the lads among the credulous crowds who dutifully paid their 25p and went in to gawp.

But the real mermaid – who is she? Lovely to look at, emerging from the water and making sweet sounds, the two obvious candidates among my patients are the seal and the dolphin. With their large friendly eyes and tendency to bob upright when at the surface, these inquisitive animals fill many of the requirements though they don't possess flowing green hair nor do they habitually carry combs and looking-glasses. Both seals and dolphins have voices, of course, and hunters such as the eskimo, since time immemorial, have listened to submarine seal songs by dipping an oar in the water and putting their ear to it. Seventy per cent of my professional time is spent looking after the dolphin and seal families and to that extent perhaps I could term myself a 'mer-vet'. After all folk used to believe in 'Sea-Bishops' and 'Sea-Monks' in days gone by, as well as mermaids. The medical care of cetaceans, the whale, dolphin and porpoise families, is undoubtedly the greatest challenge in exotic animal science. When I went, accompanied by my secretary Edith Gillon, to look at and touch my first dolphin (at Morecambe Marineland about 1965) little was known about these illustrious animals. In the past twenty years, however, the advances in our understanding, mainly due to the immense research effort injected by the US Navy, has got us to the point where it is said that we know more about the dolphin than any other animal except man and the dog!

Seals, cute little creatures though they seem to the uninitiated observer, are actually quite stroppy individuals who can and will bite nastily. Don't be deceived by those gorgeous rolling eyes! I handle them with very great respect. Most of the work I do with seals, principally the grey and common species off the British coasts, concerns combating their pre-disposition to parasites, particularly a thin black lungworm that can infest the animals and produce fatal pneumonia and also the important business of artificially rearing orphan or stranded seal pups. One of my rescued seal patients belongs to Mademoiselle Brigit Bardot, a very dedicated animal welfare lady nowadays, and lives in the marineland not far from her villa at St Tropez. The key to rearing the youngest seals is *not* to use any form of cow's milk in the diet – it upsets their digestion, often fatally, because they do not have the necessary enzymes to digest milk sugar. Instead, with the aid of an electric blender we mix filleted herring, cod liver oil, vitamins and water into an appropriate seal milk substitute that can be given by stomach tube. In recent years, we have been switching increasingly to very early weaning of the pups, moving them over on to solid food in the form of whole sprats after the first fortnight of life. They quickly get the idea of swallowing the fish voluntarily.

But the likeliest candidate among existing creatures for the title of 'ye olde and original mermaid' is, I think, the sea cow, that shy, harmless, little known animal that comes in two genera, the dugong from East Africa, Asia, the Far East and Australia and the manatee, an inhabitant of waters off West Africa and parts of South America and the Caribbean. Having a common ancestor with the elephant and grazing on seaweed (the long green hair of legend?), these gentle giants (weights up to 900 kilograms) may at first glance appear unlikely sea-maidens to be encountered by mariners, even though the latter were often away from home for years at a time, deprived of female company and possessing fertile imaginations. But they do sometimes float upright in the water cuddling their young to their breasts to suckle, much in the way that women do. The mammary glands of manatees and dugongs lie between the front flippers in the same position as in humans and elephants. Their faces, though perhaps not beautiful by Miss World standards and bearing smallish eyes, are cute to me. And remember, those sailors had been at sea a long time! The external genitalia resemble those of the woman and cases of bestiality between men and sea cows are recorded. When I was in Pakistan visiting fishing villages near Karachi, I found the local men hesitant in talking of the dugongs in the area. 'We must be careful,' they said, when I winkled it out of them. 'It is an embarrassing subject. Our women folk are jealous of the sea cows and fear some of us take them as lovers.'

The manatee found in Florida waters is, like the other sea cow species, under threat of extinction. Apart from chemical pollution, the biggest risk to their survival are tourists who, by riding about in boats looking for the endangered animals, disturb their peaceful social life and, worse, injure them accidentally with their vessels. I have seen many manatees killed or severely injured by spinning propellers. On one of my frequent visits to the everglades in the early seventies I went out with Jesse, one of the vets from Miami Seaquarium, to see what could be done for a manatee bull lying badly wounded in a creek near Collier City. When we arrived on the scene a crowd of perhaps forty was gathered on the bank, talking excitedly about what might or might not be done with the dark grey sausage lying trembling on a shelf of mud surrounded by water in which floated empty 7-Up cans and other detritus. Across the middle of the back of the manatee were two clean cuts as if by a sabre that went deep into the flesh. Blood welled slowly from their depths and overflowed to run in a sheet down one flank of the animal. It breathed heavily emitting a low grunt every half minute or so. My colleague and I jumped into the shallow water (for me it was as usual an underpants job) and waded over to the sea cow which seemed oblivious of our presence. While Jesse pulled cottonwool out of the pockets of his jacket and began swabbing the wounds, I went to the manatee's head and stroked the wide benign muzzle with its stubble of sensitive whiskers. One of the minor joys of life is having one's hand nuzzled, and if possible sucked, by a manatee's warm and delicate mouth. But the bull was in no condition to nuzzle anybody. He felt cold and was obviously badly shocked.

'I'll get the instruments,' said Jesse. 'Look – that bloody propeller's cut down to the tops of the spinal vertebrae!' He waded back and went over to his car while I inspected the gaping wounds with shining white bone now exposed at their bottom.

'Whatcha gonna do, Doc?' called someone among the spectators.

'Stitch him up!' I shouted back tersely.

'Would you spread that wound with your fingers and look this way smiling so I can zoom in, Doc!' cried a fat woman in a purple bikini and gigantic sunglasses pointing at her camera. I ignored her. 'Say, can you pull me one of that walrus's whiskers for me, Doc?' yelled a man. 'Kids back home are crazy about animals!' Thank God for the water surrounding the manatee on its patch of mud, I thought. Those creatures would have taken it to pieces for souvenirs by now if they got near it. Jesse came back with a surgical kit and while he worked on one wound I sutured the other after first flooding the hole and injecting the surrounding tissues with lignocaine local anaesthetic. It took us an hour to repair the manatee's mutilated back and when we'd finished it sported 204 nylon stitches in two long rows. Stitches that would never be removed. We gave antibiotics and cortisone and then came the strenuous bit. Pushing and heaving, the two of us, aided only by the squealing and shouts of the audience, slowly managed to move the great bulk off the mud and into the water. Once afloat the manatee drifted motionless for a few minutes and we stood watching it, fearing the worst. But then to our relief it waved its round paddle of a tail and glided down and away. But it wasn't quite a wave of goodbye, for just as it was about to disappear in the dark water the bull suddenly wheeled through 180 degrees and to my delighted amazement cruised straight at me – and nuzzled my left kneecap for several seconds! No, I'm not going to accept it was merely briefly disoriented, for the animal then turned again and swam steadily out of our sight. The crowd on the bank cheered enthusiastically. I felt like a million dollars. After all I had just indubitably been kissed farewell by a lovely real-life mermaid!

The book of Job says that 'the wild asses did stand in the high places, they snuffed up the wind like dragons'. I've been called to treat Nubian wild asses in Israel but I've also dealt with dragons.

Do the legends of fire-breathing dragons recall some distant folk memory of a time when early man perhaps encountered dinosaurs of some kind that had not become extinct at the dawn of the Age of Mammals? Surely, although it is in many ways dragon-like and a survivor from the days when the great reptiles ruled the earth, the crocodile is not the basis of the fable. Man has always known, feared and sometimes worshipped the croc. But the mysterious dragon was literally something else. But what? Seventy years ago the Western world heard for the first time of a real dragon said to be living on islands in Indonesia. Up to 15 feet long, hunting and feeding on pigs and deer and dwelling in underground tunnels, it sounded like the authentic thing although there was no mention of flaming nostrils and its discovery caused a wave of excitement among the zoological fraternity. The great reptile, largest by far of known living lizards, was popularly named the Komodo Dragon. Wisely and heavily protected by the Indonesian Government, few of these amazing animals are ever put on display in zoological collections. Over the years, I have attended six Komodo Dragon patients and find working with them an awesome experience compared with any other sort of big lizard such as rhinoceros, iguanas or Bengal water monitors.

The most impressive of the six is the 9-foot long male Komodo living at Madrid Zoo and one of a pair presented as a gift by the Indonesian Government. They arrived in 1982 straight from the wild and covered with ticks. At once, my colleagues Liliana and Antonio-Luis, the resident vets at Madrid, and I began a feverish programme of special nutrition and preventive medicine to build the animals up, rid them of parasites and hopefully aim towards breeding from the rare creatures. It is a curious thing that rare beasts so often suffer from rare ailments. My assistant, Chris

Furley, had lost two young dragons at Al Ain Zoo in 1980 from a little known and deep fungus infection. We were determined to keep the Madrid pair free of such pestilences if at all possible and housed them behind glass in a suitably hot and humid habitat with great attention paid to hygiene both in food preparation and daily cleaning of the dragon lair.

In 1983, however, the male, a powerful fellow with dark grey skin that has the texture of fresh lychee peel and baleful intelligent eyes, began to vomit. Food, in the form of dead day-old chicks or my famous steak tartare lubricated with cod liver oil for easy swallowing, just wouldn't stay on his stomach and being unable to retain much nourishment, he began to lose weight dramatically. At first I had little to go on apart from tests on the dragon's droppings. There wasn't much of interest to be found in them but I did see some yeast cells and a number of wriggling Trichomonas protozoans (the sort of bug that causes irritating genital problems in women) under the microscope and wondered if they were playing any part in the sickness. Giving drugs such as stomach sedatives and anti-Trichomonas compounds by mouth simply to have them regurgitated a few minutes later was plainly a waste of time, so I reluctantly decided on a course of injections for the dragon. Wrestling with such a big and dangerous creature would do neither it nor us much good. A bite from a Komodo can do terrible damage, easily slicing off a hand at one crunch of the heavily muscled jaws. These megalizards whose teeth really do look like dragon's teeth, all identical and curved wickedly backwards, can after all tackle full grown pigs and goats and are thought on rare occasions to have killed human beings. Antonio-Luis is a first-rate jabber of tricky animals. With the aid of a square of wooden board to protect our legs we managed to pin the Komodo into a corner of its lair with the long spiny tail protruding beyond the board's edge. My friend caught hold of it and, while it thrashed violently, moved with the tail and injected the drug as I strained to keep the dragon's body away from us. In the days that followed Antonio-Luis continued the injections, sometimes even sneaking up on the dragon while it slept and bravely giving it a shot in the tail without protection of the board or anything else and before the reptile could react, whip round and snap. But the drugs we used, chemicals to depress the vomiting centre in the brain, antibiotics and antiparasitic drugs seemed to have little effect. The monster continued to bring back its food and lose weight. Something drastic had to be done. I had to have a look inside its stomach. And that meant anaesthesia and the passing of a fibre-optic endoscope down the throat. What anaesthetic would be safe for a Komodo Dragon? Once again, as had happened previously with Chang-Chang the giant panda at Madrid, I was faced with making a fateful decision in my choice of drugs. No one knew anything about knocking out dragons. I would have to risk it, picking a drug and a dose that related in some way to my experiences with smaller, humbler lizards such as the green iguanas that I'd often operated on for damaged toes, thick legs and all manner of skin tumours.

'Don't worry,' Hanne remarked, when I told her about my concern over the anaesthesia, 'it was St George not St David who slew dragons. You'll get it right!' So putting my trust in the support of my patron saint, I decided to use the drug ketamine to immobilise the virtually priceless dragon.

Using the board again we injected him in the tail and then stood back to wait. Eventually after half an hour the big fellow fell asleep. Cautiously I crept up to him and gave him a gentle prod in the ribs. He didn't rouse. The ketamine had worked and I had my first chance to really run my hands over the biggest lizard I'd ever seen this side of the old film 'The Lost World'. It was a very special moment. To touch that long flat head and then the knobbly, cool skin, the hard muscle that filled the tail and the steely claws was quite exquisite. We loaded the unconscious dragon into a long box and trucked him over to the zoo's animal hospital. There in the operating room I checked his vital functions and with some relief found that his three-chambered reptilian heart was making all the right noises and his lungs were pumping slow but strong, though there was no sign of any fiery breath! After X-raying the dragon from tip of nose to tip of tail, I put a rubber wedge in his mouth and had a marvellous view of the rows of wicked teeth as I gently passed the lubricated fibre-optic tube over the back of the yellow tongue and down the gullet. Through the eyepiece I watched as if in some strange Tunnel of Love, the journey down a narrow pink cavern. I, or rather the lens that was my proxy, emerged abruptly into the stomach and I moved the instrument's tip around by controlling the levers at my end of the endoscope to get a good view of this mysterious grotto. At once I saw that its wet walls were of an unnaturally dirty red colour with purple patches of congestion here and there. I couldn't see any ulcers and there was nothing and nobody but me down there! The state of the stomach walls intrigued me, so taking a long cable forceps I passed it down one of the channels of the instrument until I could see it 'beside me' when I looked through the eyepiece. Then I opened its mini-crocodile jaws, nipped off a tiny piece of the wall lining and pulled it back up the tube. The fragment of tissue, a biopsy, would have to be examined microscopically. While Liliana dealt with that I took blood samples and throat swabs and then poked and pressed all over the dragon's belly looking for signs of enlarged organs. But beyond distinct signs of dehydration, there was nothing. When the Komodo suddenly blinked an eye and looked at me I gave it some more ketamine and it went under again. To combat dehydration I pumped glucose saline solution fortified with vitamins under its skin and I force fed it by stomach tube what looked like *gazpacho* made out of beef tea and raw eggs. After twenty minutes Liliana brought her microscope into the operating room and suggested I look at the bit of dragon stomach wall she'd prepared.

'*Mire*!' she said, 'look at those little fellows, David!' I peered down the microscope. There were the typical lining cells of a lizard's stomach but among them, shades of my first lesson in biology at Manchester Grammar School, were the simple outlines, familiar to every schoolboy of amoeba. Hundreds of them. But these weren't the harmless amoebas I used to search for in pond water on summer afternoons.

'The dragon's got amoeba infection,' I said to my friend. '*Entamoeba invadens*, damn it! That's why the Komodo vomits so. Don't take him back to his lair until its been disinfected with permanganate!'

The animal had almost certainly been carrying the parasites when it left Indonesia but now they were really making hay in the stomach wall. I decided to try, again with no certain knowledge of the effect on a dragon, of emetine, an old-fashioned remedy that is usually very effective against such amoeba. Daily injections of the drug would be necessary for sometime after I returned to England. Once again I was lucky. The emetine, not the mildest of chemicals, didn't produce any side-effects in the Komodo and Antonio-Luis faithfully administered the stuff each day, nearly but not quite getting bitten on many occasions. Slowly the vomiting diminished and then stopped. The dragon's appetite burgeoned and it began to put on weight again. It seemed that we'd killed off the amoeba in the nick of time. It hadn't been a very complicated case and attacks by amoebas on reptiles are not rare. But to me, the fact that we had reversed the traditional ending to the legend by saving rather than slaying the terrible monster, and done something however little in helping to conserve such endangered and fantastic animals, was all that counted.

There are unfortunately other monsters that I've never come across: the Chimaera that Homer described as having a goat's body, a lion's head and a dragon's tail; the Chichivache, the creature mentioned by Chaucer as living only on good women and that was all skin and bone because its food was so extremely scarce; the Cockatrice, whose very look caused instant death; the Echidna, not the curious little spiny anteater from Australia that you can see in the Clore Pavilion at London Zoo, but something half woman and half serpent; and the Foot Monsters of Italian romance whose feet were so big that they carried them over their heads as umbrellas. I don't miss them to be honest. The flesh and blood animals of all sorts and shapes and sizes that fill my life give me thrills and delights enough and every one is wondrous after his own particular fashion.

I should perhaps add as a postscript that although I hadn't come across any smoke and flames inside the dragon, I think that there must have been something fierce within its stomach for I found the endoscope picture to be cloudy after its use on that occasion in Madrid. Something, probably powerful acid digestive juices, had pitted the surface of the instrument's glass lens tip. It had to go for repair. So perhaps dragon's breath or at least its spittle does in a sense burn!

13 *A Lion-Tamer Tamer*

In the beginning were the lion tamers. For a young vet called to a circus, the principal baptism of fire was an encounter with the man who 'tamed' – unpleasant word in the connotations of those days – or trained the big cats. Almost without exception the old time lion trainers regarded themselves and indeed were regarded by their fellow artistes as the stars of any circus troupe. Gnarled of mind, such macho prima donnas had little time for veterinary surgeons of any sort and particularly eschewed ones, like me, that were ringing wet behind the ears. They could force potions down full-grown lions without need of sedatives and pull teeth with a net and a crowbar. Hadn't circuses bred lions and tigers in the days when zoos found it difficult and safari parks hadn't been thought of? No, up to the early sixties the lion trainer, almost always self-styled Captain something or other, was considered to be *the* animal man of the circus, ever ready to cast with disdain pearls of wisdom on other species such as horses or elephants and their peculiar problems before swine such as me, MRCVS.

Such an individual was Captain Eppler of Bishop's Circus. Physically he was the epitome of his kind. Medium height with a wiry build, a craggy face and flinty eyes set under red and watery lids, he affected thin and waxed moustachios and brilliantined his hair. There was something most definitely military about his bearing though he'd never been in the army. He always wore jodhpurs and I suspect may have slept in them. His voice was loud and his speech clipped and littered with obscenities. A lady's man and a dark rum drinker, he had a gentle, untidy and voluminous ex-trapeze artist as a wife and they lived together in a caravan plastered with fading photographs of himself with cats – lions, tigers, leopards, jaguars and pumas – and folk like the Pope, landladies, Cockney comedians and forgotten film stars. He took, typically, an aversion to me the moment he first saw me.

I had been called to the circus, which was encamped on a muddy field near the centre of Bolton, to attend a bear with an angry boil on its bottom. On arrival I wandered into the circle of caravans around the Big Top and spotted a figure in jodhpurs and carrying a short cane stick under his arm walking towards me.

'Good evening, can you tell me where I can find the boss?' I said. The man stopped, put his legs apart and started tapping the upturned palm of one hand with the stick. He reminded me of a Nazi commandant in one of those escape films.

'Who's asking?' came the barked reply.

'Er . . . I am. The vet. Come to see a bear.' Eppler, for it was he, spat expertly to one side and snorted dramatically.

'Vet eh? Know a b—— thing about bears then do you?' Beginning to rile I swung my medical case in front of me.

'I asked to see Mr Bishop, the boss. Not bandy words with . . . ' I bit my tongue. 'Er . . . you're not Mr Bishop are you?' Eppler gave a bitter laugh in lieu of a reply.

'Vets!' he said, 'I've 'ad 'em. Killed more cats than I've had 'ot dinners!' Then, again in the typical style of the verbal sallies launched at first meeting by one of his profession, added, 'The only vet I'd let touch my tigers was Mr Fountain. Charlie Fountain. They don't make 'em like that any more. Took a gangrened b—— toe off a Bengal male my Dad was working when I was a lad. B—— clever Mr Charlie. Do you know 'im?' Considering I was under 30 at the time, and Fountain whoever he was must have been by now in his nineties, it was hardly likely.

'The boss, where is his caravan?' I repeated.

'That bear doesn't need a b—— vet, my lad,' continued Eppler. 'Boils on their arses are as common as goosegobs in July. Put some rock sulphur in their water, that's what it b—— needs. You take my advice and . . . '

'Look!' I interrupted angrily. 'Will you tell me where the boss is, or should I go and find that bear myself? This isn't the only call I've got to make tonight!'

Glaring ferociously, the lion trainer pointed his stick at one of the caravans' doors. 'Knock on there, sonny,' he snarled, 'and let's hope they don't come running for me when that b—— bear bites your b—— balls off!' He quick marched away.

I found Bishop, the circus boss, and introduced myself. He seemed, in contrast to the fellow I'd just met, to be a humane and friendly individual of considerable intelligence who was concerned for the well-being of all the animals in his company. Over a cup of tea after I'd examined the bear in a crush cage, given an injection of penicillin, clipped the hair over the abscess and left instructions for frequent fomentations of hot water and Epsom Salts, he asked me about my interest in wild animals.

'We could do with more up-to-date doctoring in the circus,' he remarked. 'There's too much reliance on the older mumbo-jumbo ways. And the vets we meet going from town to town don't show much interest in our livestock. Not that I don't understand their problems with us fly-by-nights. No chance to follow up cases or learn anything, with us here today and gone tomorrow.'

'Do you still enjoy this nomadic circus life?' I asked. He smiled wistfully.

'Been in it all my life. And my parents before me. But times are changing fast. Y'know, more and more I think of someday quitting and taking all the animals, settling down and opening a zoo or one of those lion parks that my mate Jimmy Chipperfield keeps going on about.' As things turned out, Bishop did in fact open a large safari park of his own some years later. Before I left his caravan the circus boss asked me to come again the following day when it was light and inspect all the animals on site. 'It strikes me as a good idea to have a keen young fellow like you run the rule over 'em – see if there is anything we should be doing that we aren't,' he said. I agreed to come after the matinee performance and making sure that I collected my fee in cash ('Only give credit to Chipperfields, Bertram Mills, Smarts and God in the circus world,' my then partner Norman Whittle used to insist), drove home.

In the late afternoon of the next day I went back to the circus and walked round all the animals with Bishop. At first my impression was of overall good husbandry and cleanliness. I commented on the sparkling condition of the liberty horses, pointed out a patch of eczema on an elephant's tail that needed attention, suggested changes in the vitamin and mineral supplementation of the big cats' diet and aired my strong reservations about the suitability of bears, under any circumstances, as circus animals. The circus owner listened intently and made notes of my suggestions. Then, we arrived at the big cats. The ferocious-looking character in the jodhpurs was putting some lions through their paces in a training ring which had been erected near the big cat wagons. He held a long whip in one hand and the cane stick in the other.

'Bella come on! Samson down! Samson DOWN!' he bellowed with a brassy voice as we stood watching through the wall of vertical bars. When he caught sight of me with the boss he gave a thin sneer and cracked his whip before looking away.

'Any problems with the cats, Mr Eppler?' called Bishop. 'I've got the vet here, doing a check-up.' Eppler wheeled round towards us and looked fit to vomit fire and brimstone.

'The vet, Mr Bishop?' he rasped eventually, after sending a lion charging towards me and brushing the other side of the bars a hand's-breadth from my face with its whiskers. 'What's wrong with my cats?'

'Nobody's saying anything's wrong with them, Carl,' said Bishop soothingly. 'Just that while Doctor Taylor's here, we might as well use him if you've got any problems!'

Eppler grinned mirthlessly. 'Fifty-one years in the business Mr Bishop. Barnhams, Ringlands, Krone – I've worked with 'em all. I don't think there's much I'll be learning from a young vet from this b—— part of the world whose never been in a ring with anything bigger than a b—— Lancashire Heeler.'

'No need to be bolshy, Carl!' said Bishop sternly. 'We can all still learn something no matter how much experience we've got.'

'Maybe – all right then!' replied Eppler putting the lions back on their pedestals. 'If that young lad there knows so much, can he tell me how to train a leopard to ride on the back of a tiger? Can he cure star-gazing lions with oils of camphor like my Dad could?' I turned away silently in exasperation and looked at the tigers resting in their travelling wagons.

'Carl, that's not the point!' said the circus boss. 'No one is saying you don't know your cats but . . . '

'But . . .' I interrupted loudly, 'look at these cat wagons Mr Bishop!' He turned round. 'They're filthy! Blood, hair and fat engrained in the wood! They've not been cleaned for weeks! And there's some old tiger droppings over there that are growing mould. Health risk Mr Bishop – the place must be alive with salmonella bugs and worse!' We both looked at Eppler. I thought for a moment that he would ascend heavenwards like a rocket out of his trim brown jodhpurs. His flinty eyes turned into grey smoking gun barrels.

'What the b—— are you talking about, sonny?' he spluttered.

'This dirt, this mess, this ordure!' I said slowly, knowing I was on a winner.

'I've kept hundreds, thousands of lions and tigers in those wagons without trouble. How many big cats have you . . .?'

'Carl!' snapped Bishop coldly. 'Cut the crap! Get those wagons cleaned like the vet says!'

'And use some disinfectant,' I added as a *coup de grâce* and feeling cock-a-hoop. We walked on and I heard Eppler behind us start bawling his frustration on the poor lions.

'Bella! B—— well come on!'

'Sorry about that, Doc,' said Bishop. 'Eppler's a bit of a martinet I'm afraid but there's no better trainer of cats in England. You can rest assured though that I'll see he cleans and disinfects those wagons before the weekend.' There wasn't much else amiss in Bishop's circus and when I'd seen all the animals we went over the list of points to be attended to. 'Won't you stay to watch the next performance?' asked Bishop as we sat drinking coffee in his caravan. 'We've got Karah Khavak, the best crocodile hypnotist on the continent, touring with us at the moment.'

'I'd love to,' I replied, 'but I must get back. A giraffe at Belle Vue is likely to go into labour tonight.'

Three days later at breakfast time on a Sunday morning I received a frantic 'phone call from Bishop's principal clown. 'We're in Blackburn now, sir,' gasped the fellow as he crammed pennies into the coin box, 'and one of the lions has just had a heart attack! Mr Bishop says can you come straight away!' I gulped down a mouthful of kipper and pulled on my jacket. Everything I might need was in the car. Heart attack in a lion – now that, if it were true, would be a most interesting case! As I drove over the moors through Edenfield and then Haslingden, I reviewed in my mind the cases of lion illness that I'd treated in the six years or so since qualifying. Not a lot. Lions appear to be hardy, uncomplaining cats who took the cuts and scratches of family squabbles in their stride and rarely developed septic infections. They could eat the greenest, most foul-smelling knacker meat and suffer not so much as a bit of dyspepsia. As the poet and mystic William Blake observed, 'the fox provides for himself but God provides for the lion'. It's just as well that God does, for lions, much as I love them, are lazy, lackadaisical folk who really do like their lunches brought to them – even in the wild.

It was raining heavily when I turned into the park where the circus had been newly pitched. I drove through a gap in the ring of caravans and pulled up close to the lion wagon. Inside one of the bar-fronted compartments I saw Eppler and Bishop crouched on their haunches over what looked like a dead lion.

'Quick!' shouted Bishop as I got out of the car and was instantly swept with driving rain that soaked me to the skin before I could get on my waterproofs, 'He's still with us!' I squelched through the mud and clambered into the lion wagon. The atmosphere was heavy with ammonia from the night urine of a dozen big cats. It made my eyes water. But at least it was dry in there.

'Heart attack, sonny!' barked Eppler as I knelt beside the supine barely conscious lion and felt its pulse. 'Mr Fountain would give it some belladonna pretty damn sharp!' I took the stethoscope out of my case and began listening to the chest sounds. The skin of the mature male lion felt terribly cold and there was foam around its mighty muzzle.

'It's had convulsions too,' said Bishop quietly. 'What do you think is the matter?'

'Heart attack. Seen it when your arse was the size of a shirt button, my lad. Belladonna is what the old lion vets gave!' Eppler spat accurately between the bars. I pulled down one of the big cat's eyelids. Was it a trick of the light or was there really a bit of jaundice yellow under the pink?

'It's collapsed and almost in a coma,' I said. 'Could be several causes but it's *not* the heart – that's sound as a bell.'

'Heart attack!' repeated Eppler venomously. 'Pity old Mr Fountain's retired to Bath now. Could have rung him!'

I looked round the wagon. The ancient dirt and excrement had gone. It had obviously been washed down recently for the walls were still damp. 'Mr Eppler made a good job of it didn't he?' said Bishop as he saw me registering the improvement.

'Bahh!' grated the lion trainer. 'Book learning! Never was anything wrong with the b—— wagons. And now we've got Samson here down with a heart attack. He's a gonna for sure!'

I opened my case and took out syringes, needles, some Pastrum and a bottle of saline for a drip. As I filled the syringe with Pastrum to boost the circulation, I noticed that a trickle of water from the newly washed wall had collected into a puddle on a patch of floor free of sawdust. The little puddle was milky white. Instinctively I dipped my finger into it and sniffed. There was the characteristic odour of carbolic acid.

'Hey! Mr Eppler!' I said sharply. 'What kind of disinfectant did you use on the wagons?'

Eppler gave a wild cackle, 'Can't you think about anything but b—— cleaning and disinfectant, sonny? There's a b—— lion dying in front of you with a b—— heart attack!'

'What disinfectant?' I repeated loudly. 'I *must know*!'

The lion trainer rolled his eyes and gestured to a can standing on the ground outside. 'That sonny. That! Black disinfectant, the best – don't start quibbling about that! I know what's right for my cats!'

I jumped down from the wagon and picked up the half-empty tin. It was typical phenol-based agricultural disinfectant. Great for use around farms, stables and kennels and lethal to bugs of all kinds.

'Don't waste your time sonny! Get some belladonna!' yelled Eppler. 'That stuff will have killed any germs in here if that's what you're worried about. But this is a heart attack, mark my words!'

I dropped the can and turned towards Eppler with the rain streaming down my face. 'Mr Eppler' I said as calmly as I could, 'you, with all your experience, your knowledge, your insight into life have made a big, big BALLS-UP!'

'What do you mean?' he said spitting the words out.

'You have used this disinfectant and . . .'

'Bull dust! It's what my father used! Mr Fountain did as well for his horses. It's on the label – for all kinds of animal disease. Come off it, sonny!'

'You're right Mr Eppler,' I continued, 'it is excellent for general use with animals but there's one snag. If you don't rinse off well, phenol chemicals can be taken into the body through the skin – *of cats* – lions and tigers as well as moggies – and kill them!'

Eppler said nothing but looked thunderstruck. 'You mean the lion's poisoned?' said Bishop, as I climbed back into the wagon.

'Yes. Must have lain in a puddle of disinfectant or just possibly licked it. We're looking at a case of phenol poisoning. Mr Eppler's disinfectant.'

'What can you do, Doctor?' I didn't at first recognise Eppler's voice. He spoke quietly now and suddenly like an old man.

'Get me some bottles of milk, buckets of water, soapflakes and lots of towels!' I answered. 'We'll have to see if we can clear any phenol out of his guts and off his skin.'

Eppler obediently slipped away. While he was gone I set up the drip and gave the Pastrum intravenously. When the lion trainer returned with the items I'd ordered we set to work doing two things that would have looked extremely odd to any observer. First I pumped out its stomach with several pints of milk through a stomach tube and then the three of us gave a bedbath to the lion from tip to toe. 'Scrub hard! Work up plenty of foam!' I said, as we pummelled away at the Lord of the Jungle as if he were a film star in a bubblebath, enveloping him in foaming clouds of soapy lather. I had Eppler dashing to and fro from the lion wagon with more buckets of warm water for the rinsing. 'Now Mr Eppler,' I said when that was done, 'rub him with towels as hard as you can. Dry him thoroughly – we don't want him to catch pneumonia. And when you've done that please run a line from the nearest caravan and put one of the ladies' hair driers on to him to finish the job.'

'Right you are, Doc,' murmured the lion trainer. When the blow drying was completed I instructed him to sit with the lion and turn him over every thirty minutes to avoid lung congestion. By teatime of that day we had the cleanest lion you can ever imagine and the warm water and rubbing had done wonders in helping the drugs to improve his circulation. Samson began to make throaty noises and flick an ear occasionally. 'Do you think he'll make it?' Eppler asked, as I set up another bottle on the drip. I looked at the lion and saw the pink tongue curl briefly round his upper lip.

'Possibly,' I replied. 'You'll have to stay up with him all night, of course.'

'Anything you say, Doc!'

It was a a long haul but Samson the lion did eventually make it. Eppler nursed him assiduously and did everything I asked without question. A few weeks later, I was standing at the back of the Big Top with Bishop watching a performance while Eppler was in the ring surrounded by Samson and a mixed group of tigers and lions. 'Done all right hasn't he, that lion?' remarked the circus boss.

'Seems like it,' I answered, feeling rather proud.

'Eppler's quite a fan of yours now by the way – he's going around telling everyone how he taught you everything you know!'

'That's all right,' I said, 'I'm now a qualified lion-tamer tamer,' and we both laughed.

14 Another Day

The writing down of all this looks like going on indefinitely, for every day brings something new, something unexpected in the world of animals and their medical problems. As I write I have just received the great news that Jane, the orang-outang mother who had post-natal depression all those years ago at Belle Vue, has given birth to a healthy little baby in San Diego Zoo where she now resides. What memories I have of her and all her children including 'Amy', the one that survived and had to be bottle reared. My elder daughter Stephanie has just qualified as a medical doctor and wants to specialise in gynaecology. It would be a supreme satisfaction to call her in one day to work on another 'Jane' with me. There's a report of trouble with a herd of gazelle in Abu Dhabi. We've identified the important disease called Malta Fever in them, but the Sheikh, their owner, doesn't believe us and wants a specialist in Indian ayurvedic herbal medicine called in – I must fly out to give Chris, my assistant, moral support. Juno, the baby dolphin born at Windsor, and one of the same age that I look after near Hannover in Germany, are both doing well at 20 weeks of age and we are using an advanced ultrasonic scanner on 'Honey', another Windsor dolphin, to monitor her pregnancy. I suppose I'll be her midwife in 1985. Last night a lady from Wisconsin, USA, 'phoned – her pet serval had just broken its leg. This morning I inserted a new contraceptive implant under the skin of a female tiger at Chessington. Tomorrow I fly to Italy to do some chiropody on a giraffe. Meanwhile, the 'One By One' filming for the second series continues, in episode six of which I make my debut as script writer and one of us has to be on location whenever animals are used. Next week, I'll be playing with Chu-Lin, the baby panda at Madrid and doing a colonoscopy on his step-father Chang-Chang in front of Border Television's 'Nature Trail' cameras, and very soon I'll be presenting the Animal Spot again for TVS's Saturday morning 'Number 73' show. Somewhere for sure in the near future all manner of animals await. There will be surprises, delights, tragedies and disappointments. I will learn much and constantly see things I don't understand. One thing is certain – I'll tell you all about it in due course, if the Killer whales, Komodo dragons and King cobras don't catch me napping!